TEACHER'S GUIDE

Connected Mathematics 2™

W9-CUA-720

Data About Us

Statistics

Glenda Lappan
James T. Fey
William M. Fitzgerald
Susan N. Friel
Elizabeth Difanis Phillips

PEARSON

Boston, Massachusetts · Glenview, Illinois · Shoreview, Minnesota · Upper Saddle River, New Jersey

Connected Mathematics™ was developed at Michigan State University with financial support from the Michigan State University Office of the Provost, Computing and Technology, and the College of Natural Science.

This material is based upon work supported by the National Science Foundation under Grant No. MDR 9150217 and Grant No. ESI 9986372. Opinions expressed are those of the authors and not necessarily those of the Foundation.

The Michigan State University authors and administration have agreed that all MSU royalties arising from this publication will be devoted to purposes supported by the Department of Mathematics and the MSU Mathematics Enrichment Fund.

13-digit ISBN 978-0-13-366191-0
10-digit ISBN 0-13-366191-1
2 3 4 5 6 7 8 9 10   11 10 09 08

Authors of Connected Mathematics

(from left to right) Glenda Lappan, Betty Phillips, Susan Friel, Bill Fitzgerald, Jim Fey

Glenda Lappan is a University Distinguished Professor in the Department of Mathematics at Michigan State University. Her research and development interests are in the connected areas of students' learning of mathematics and mathematics teachers' professional growth and change related to the development and enactment of K–12 curriculum materials.

James T. Fey is a Professor of Curriculum and Instruction and Mathematics at the University of Maryland. His consistent professional interest has been development and research focused on curriculum materials that engage middle and high school students in problem-based collaborative investigations of mathematical ideas and their applications.

William M. Fitzgerald (*Deceased*) was a Professor in the Department of Mathematics at Michigan State University. His early research was on the use of concrete materials in supporting student learning and led to the development of teaching materials for laboratory environments. Later he helped develop a teaching model to support student experimentation with mathematics.

Susan N. Friel is a Professor of Mathematics Education in the School of Education at the University of North Carolina at Chapel Hill. Her research interests focus on statistics education for middle-grade students and, more broadly, on teachers' professional development and growth in teaching mathematics K–8.

Elizabeth Difanis Phillips is a Senior Academic Specialist in the Mathematics Department of Michigan State University. She is interested in teaching and learning mathematics for both teachers and students. These interests have led to curriculum and professional development projects at the middle school and high school levels, as well as projects related to the teaching and learning of algebra across the grades.

CMP2 Development Staff

Teacher Collaborator in Residence
Yvonne Grant
Michigan State University

Administrative Assistant
Judith Martus Miller
Michigan State University

Production and Field Site Manager
Lisa Keller
Michigan State University

Technical and Editorial Support
Brin Keller, Peter Lappan, Jim Laser,
Michael Masterson, Stacey Miceli

Assessment Team
June Bailey and Debra Sobko (Apollo Middle School, Rochester, New York), George Bright (University of North Carolina, Greensboro), Gwen Ranzau Campbell (Sunrise Park Middle School, White Bear Lake, Minnesota), Holly DeRosia, Kathy Dole, and Teri Keusch (Portland Middle School, Portland, Michigan), Mary Beth Schmitt (Traverse City East Junior High School, Traverse City, Michigan), Genni Steele (Central Middle School, White Bear Lake, Minnesota), Jacqueline Stewart (Okemos, Michigan), Elizabeth Tye (Magnolia Junior High School, Magnolia, Arkansas)

Development Assistants
At Lansing Community College *Undergraduate Assistant:* James Brinegar

At Michigan State University *Graduate Assistants:* Dawn Berk, Emily Bouck, Bulent Buyukbozkirli, Kuo-Liang Chang, Christopher Danielson, Srinivasa Dharmavaram, Deb Johanning, Wesley Kretzschmar, Kelly Rivette, Sarah Sword, Tat Ming Sze, Marie Turini, Jeffrey Wanko; *Undergraduate Assistants:* Daniel Briggs, Jeffrey Chapin, Jade Corsé, Elisha Hardy, Alisha Harold, Elizabeth Keusch, Julia Letoutchaia, Karen Loeffler, Brian Oliver, Carl Oliver, Evonne Pedawi, Lauren Rebrovich

At the University of Maryland *Graduate Assistants:* Kim Harris Bethea, Kara Karch

At the University of North Carolina (Chapel Hill) *Graduate Assistants:* Mark Ellis, Trista Stearns; *Undergraduate Assistant:* Daniel Smith

Advisory Board for CMP2

Thomas Banchoff
Professor of Mathematics
Brown University
Providence, Rhode Island

Anne Bartel
Mathematics Coordinator
Minneapolis Public Schools
Minneapolis, Minnesota

Hyman Bass
Professor of Mathematics
University of Michigan
Ann Arbor, Michigan

Joan Ferrini-Mundy
Associate Dean of the College of
Natural Science; Professor
Michigan State University
East Lansing, Michigan

James Hiebert
Professor
University of Delaware
Newark, Delaware

Susan Hudson Hull
Charles A. Dana Center
University of Texas
Austin, Texas

Michele Luke
Mathematics Curriculum
Coordinator
West Junior High
Minnetonka, Minnesota

Kay McClain
Assistant Professor of
Mathematics Education
Vanderbilt University
Nashville, Tennessee

Edward Silver
Professor; Chair of Educational
Studies
University of Michigan
Ann Arbor, Michigan

Judith Sowder
Professor Emerita
San Diego State University
San Diego, California

Lisa Usher
Mathematics Resource Teacher
California Academy of
Mathematics and Science
San Pedro, California

Field Test Sites for CMP2

During the development of the revised edition of *Connected Mathematics* (CMP2), more than 100 classroom teachers have field-tested materials at 49 school sites in 12 states and the District of Columbia. This classroom testing occurred over three academic years (2001 through 2004), allowing careful study of the effectiveness of each of the 24 units that comprise the program. A special thanks to the students and teachers at these pilot schools.

Arkansas
Magnolia Public Schools
Kittena Bell*, Judith Trowell*; *Central Elementary School:* Maxine Broom, Betty Eddy, Tiffany Fallin, Bonnie Flurry, Carolyn Monk, Elizabeth Tye; *Magnolia Junior High School:* Monique Bryan, Ginger Cook, David Graham, Shelby Lamkin

Colorado
Boulder Public Schools
Nevin Platt Middle School: Judith Koenig

St. Vrain Valley School District, Longmont
Westview Middle School: Colleen Beyer, Kitty Canupp, Ellie Decker*, Peggy McCarthy, Tanya deNobrega, Cindy Payne, Ericka Pilon, Andrew Roberts

District of Columbia
Capitol Hill Day School: Ann Lawrence

Georgia
University of Georgia, Athens
Brad Findell

Madison Public Schools
Morgan County Middle School: Renee Burgdorf, Lynn Harris, Nancy Kurtz, Carolyn Stewart

Maine
Falmouth Public Schools
Falmouth Middle School: Donna Erikson, Joyce Hebert, Paula Hodgkins, Rick Hogan, David Legere, Cynthia Martin, Barbara Stiles, Shawn Towle*

Michigan
Portland Public Schools
Portland Middle School: Mark Braun, Holly DeRosia, Kathy Dole*, Angie Foote, Teri Keusch, Tammi Wardwell

Traverse City Area Public Schools
Bertha Vos Elementary: Kristin Sak; *Central Grade School:* Michelle Clark; Jody Meyers; *Eastern Elementary:* Karrie Tufts; *Interlochen Elementary:* Mary McGee-Cullen; *Long Lake Elementary:* Julie Faulkner*, Charlie Maxbauer, Katherine Sleder; *Norris Elementary:* Hope Slanaker; *Oak Park Elementary:* Jessica Steed; *Traverse Heights Elementary:* Jennifer Wolfert; *Westwoods Elementary:* Nancy Conn; *Old Mission Peninsula School:* Deb Larimer; *Traverse City East Junior High:* Ivanka Berkshire, Ruthanne Kladder, Jan Palkowski, Jane Peterson, Mary Beth Schmitt; *Traverse City West Junior High:* Dan Fouch*, Ray Fouch

Sturgis Public Schools
Sturgis Middle School: Ellen Eisele

Minnesota
Burnsville School District 191
Hidden Valley Elementary: Stephanie Cin, Jane McDevitt

Hopkins School District 270
Alice Smith Elementary: Sandra Cowing, Kathleen Gustafson, Martha Mason, Scott Stillman; *Eisenhower Elementary:* Chad Bellig, Patrick Berger, Nancy Glades, Kye Johnson, Shane Wasserman, Victoria Wilson; *Gatewood Elementary:* Sarah Ham, Julie Kloos, Janine Pung, Larry Wade; *Glen Lake Elementary:* Jacqueline Cramer, Kathy Hering, Cecelia Morris, Robb Trenda; *Katherine Curren Elementary:* Diane Bancroft, Sue DeWit, John Wilson; *L. H. Tanglen Elementary:* Kevin Athmann, Lisa Becker, Mary LaBelle, Kathy Rezac, Roberta Severson; *Meadowbrook Elementary:* Jan Gauger, Hildy Shank, Jessica Zimmerman; *North Junior High:* Laurel Hahn, Kristin Lee, Jodi Markuson, Bruce Mestemacher, Laurel Miller, Bonnie Rinker, Jeannine Salzer, Sarah Shafer, Cam Stottler; *West Junior High:* Alicia Beebe, Kristie Earl, Nobu Fujii, Pam Georgetti, Susan Gilbert, Regina Nelson Johnson, Debra Lindstrom, Michele Luke*, Jon Sorensen

Minneapolis School District 1
Ann Sullivan K–8 School: Bronwyn Collins; Anne Bartel* (Curriculum and Instruction Office)

Wayzata School District 284
Central Middle School: Sarajane Myers, Dan Nielsen, Tanya Ravnholdt

White Bear Lake School District 624
Central Middle School: Amy Jorgenson, Michelle Reich, Brenda Sammon

New York
New York City Public Schools
IS 89: Yelena Aynbinder, Chi-Man Ng, Nina Rapaport, Joel Spengler, Phyllis Tam*, Brent Wyso; *Wagner Middle School:* Jason Appel, Intissar Fernandez, Yee Gee Get, Richard Goldstein, Irving Marcus, Sue Norton, Bernadita Owens, Jennifer Rehn*, Kevin Yuhas

---

* indicates a Field Test Site Coordinator

Ohio

Talawanda School District, Oxford
Talawanda Middle School: Teresa Abrams, Larry Brock, Heather Brosey, Julie Churchman, Monna Even, Karen Fitch, Bob George, Amanda Klee, Pat Meade, Sandy Montgomery, Barbara Sherman, Lauren Steidl

Miami University
Jeffrey Wanko*

Springfield Public Schools
Rockway School: Jim Mamer

Pennsylvania

Pittsburgh Public Schools
Kenneth Labuskes, Marianne O'Connor, Mary Lynn Raith*; *Arthur J. Rooney Middle School:* David Hairston, Stamatina Mousetis, Alfredo Zangaro; *Frick International Studies Academy:* Suzanne Berry, Janet Falkowski, Constance Finseth, Romika Hodge, Frank Machi; *Reizenstein Middle School:* Jeff Baldwin, James Brautigam, Lorena Burnett, Glen Cobbett, Michael Jordan, Margaret Lazur, Tamar McPherson, Melissa Munnell, Holly Neely, Ingrid Reed, Dennis Reft

Texas

Austin Independent School District
Bedichek Middle School: Lisa Brown, Jennifer Glasscock, Vicki Massey

El Paso Independent School District
Cordova Middle School: Armando Aguirre, Anneliesa Durkes, Sylvia Guzman, Pat Holguin*, William Holguin, Nancy Nava, Laura Orozco, Michelle Peña, Roberta Rosen, Patsy Smith, Jeremy Wolf

Plano Independent School District
Patt Henry, James Wohlgehagen*; *Frankford Middle School:* Mandy Baker, Cheryl Butsch, Amy Dudley, Betsy Eshelman, Janet Greene, Cort Haynes, Kathy Letchworth, Kay Marshall, Kelly McCants, Amy Reck, Judy Scott, Syndy Snyder, Lisa Wang; *Wilson Middle School:* Darcie Bane, Amanda Bedenko, Whitney Evans, Tonelli Hatley, Sarah (Becky) Higgs, Kelly Johnston, Rebecca McElligott, Kay Neuse, Cheri Slocum, Kelli Straight

Washington

Evergreen School District
Shahala Middle School: Nicole Abrahamsen, Terry Coon*, Carey Doyle, Sheryl Drechsler, George Gemma, Gina Helland, Amy Hilario, Darla Lidyard, Sean McCarthy, Tilly Meyer, Willow Nuewelt, Todd Parsons, Brian Pederson, Stan Posey, Shawn Scott, Craig Sjoberg, Lynette Sundstrom, Charles Switzer, Luke Youngblood

Wisconsin

Beaver Dam Unified School District
Beaver Dam Middle School: Jim Braemer, Jeanne Frick, Jessica Greatens, Barbara Link, Dennis McCormick, Karen Michels, Nancy Nichols*, Nancy Palm, Shelly Stelsel, Susan Wiggins

---

* indicates a Field Test Site Coordinator

Reviews of CMP to Guide Development of CMP2

Before writing for CMP2 began or field tests were conducted, the first edition of *Connected Mathematics* was submitted to the mathematics faculties of school districts from many parts of the country and to 80 individual reviewers for extensive comments.

School District Survey Reviews of CMP

Arizona
Madison School District #38 (Phoenix)

Arkansas
Cabot School District, Little Rock School District, Magnolia School District

California
Los Angeles Unified School District

Colorado
St. Vrain Valley School District (Longmont)

Florida
Leon County Schools (Tallahassee)

Illinois
School District #21 (Wheeling)

Indiana
Joseph L. Block Junior High (East Chicago)

Kentucky
Fayette County Public Schools (Lexington)

Maine
Selection of Schools

Massachusetts
Selection of Schools

Michigan
Sparta Area Schools

Minnesota
Hopkins School District

Texas
Austin Independent School District, The El Paso Collaborative for Academic Excellence, Plano Independent School District

Wisconsin
Platteville Middle School

Individual Reviewers of CMP

Arkansas
Deborah Cramer; Robby Frizzell *(Taylor)*; Lowell Lynde *(University of Arkansas, Monticello)*; Leigh Manzer *(Norfork)*; Lynne Roberts *(Emerson High School, Emerson)*; Tony Timms *(Cabot Public Schools)*; Judith Trowell *(Arkansas Department of Higher Education)*

California
José Alcantar *(Gilroy)*; Eugenie Belcher *(Gilroy)*; Marian Pasternack *(Lowman M. S. T. Center, North Hollywood)*; Susana Pezoa *(San Jose)*; Todd Rabusin *(Hollister)*; Margaret Siegfried *(Ocala Middle School, San Jose)*; Polly Underwood *(Ocala Middle School, San Jose)*

Colorado
Janeane Golliher *(St. Vrain Valley School District, Longmont)*; Judith Koenig *(Nevin Platt Middle School, Boulder)*

Florida
Paige Loggins *(Swift Creek Middle School, Tallahassee)*

Illinois
Jan Robinson *(School District #21, Wheeling)*

Indiana
Frances Jackson *(Joseph L. Block Junior High, East Chicago)*

Kentucky
Natalee Feese *(Fayette County Public Schools, Lexington)*

Maine
Betsy Berry *(Maine Math & Science Alliance, Augusta)*

Maryland
Joseph Gagnon *(University of Maryland, College Park)*; Paula Maccini *(University of Maryland, College Park)*

Massachusetts
George Cobb *(Mt. Holyoke College, South Hadley)*; Cliff Kanold *(University of Massachusetts, Amherst)*

Michigan
Mary Bouck *(Farwell Area Schools)*; Carol Dorer *(Slauson Middle School, Ann Arbor)*; Carrie Heaney *(Forsythe Middle School, Ann Arbor)*; Ellen Hopkins *(Clague Middle School, Ann Arbor)*; Teri Keusch *(Portland Middle School, Portland)*; Valerie Mills *(Oakland Schools, Waterford)*; Mary Beth Schmitt *(Traverse City East Junior High, Traverse City)*; Jack Smith *(Michigan State University, East Lansing)*; Rebecca Spencer *(Sparta Middle School, Sparta)*; Ann Marie Nicoll Turner *(Tappan Middle School, Ann Arbor)*; Scott Turner *(Scarlett Middle School, Ann Arbor)*

Minnesota
Margarita Alvarez *(Olson Middle School, Minneapolis)*; Jane Amundson *(Nicollet Junior High, Burnsville)*; Anne Bartel *(Minneapolis Public Schools)*; Gwen Ranzau Campbell *(Sunrise Park Middle School, White Bear Lake)*; Stephanie Cin *(Hidden Valley Elementary, Burnsville)*; Joan Garfield *(University of Minnesota, Minneapolis)*; Gretchen Hall *(Richfield Middle School, Richfield)*; Jennifer Larson *(Olson Middle School, Minneapolis)*; Michele Luke *(West Junior High, Minnetonka)*; Jeni Meyer *(Richfield Junior High, Richfield)*; Judy Pfingsten *(Inver Grove Heights Middle School, Inver Grove Heights)*; Sarah Shafer *(North Junior High, Minnetonka)*; Genni Steele *(Central Middle School, White Bear Lake)*; Victoria Wilson *(Eisenhower Elementary, Hopkins)*; Paul Zorn *(St. Olaf College, Northfield)*

New York
Debra Altenau-Bartolino *(Greenwich Village Middle School, New York)*; Doug Clements *(University of Buffalo)*; Francis Curcio *(New York University, New York)*; Christine Dorosh *(Clinton School for Writers, Brooklyn)*; Jennifer Rehn *(East Side Middle School, New York)*; Phyllis Tam *(IS 89 Lab School, New York)*;

Marie Turini *(Louis Armstrong Middle School, New York)*; Lucy West *(Community School District 2, New York)*; Monica Witt *(Simon Baruch Intermediate School 104, New York)*

Pennsylvania
Robert Aglietti *(Pittsburgh)*; Sharon Mihalich *(Freeport)*; Jennifer Plumb *(South Hills Middle School, Pittsburgh)*; Mary Lynn Raith *(Pittsburgh Public Schools)*

Texas
Michelle Bittick *(Austin Independent School District)*; Margaret Cregg *(Plano Independent School District)*; Sheila Cunningham *(Klein Independent School District)*; Judy Hill *(Austin Independent School District)*; Patricia Holguin *(El Paso Independent School District)*; Bonnie McNemar *(Arlington)*; Kay Neuse *(Plano Independent School District)*; Joyce Polanco *(Austin Independent School District)*; Marge Ramirez *(University of Texas at El Paso)*; Pat Rossman *(Baker Campus, Austin)*; Cindy Schimek *(Houston)*; Cynthia Schneider *(Charles A. Dana Center, University of Texas at Austin)*; Uri Treisman *(Charles A. Dana Center, University of Texas at Austin)*; Jacqueline Weilmuenster *(Grapevine-Colleyville Independent School District)*; LuAnn Weynand *(San Antonio)*; Carmen Whitman *(Austin Independent School District)*; James Wohlgehagen *(Plano Independent School District)*

Washington
Ramesh Gangolli *(University of Washington, Seattle)*

Wisconsin
Susan Lamon *(Marquette University, Hales Corner)*; Steve Reinhart *(retired, Chippewa Falls Middle School, Eau Claire)*

Table of Contents

Data About Us
Statistics

Unit Introduction **2**
    Goals of the Unit **2**
    Developing Students' Mathematical Habits **2**
Mathematics of the Unit **3**
    Overview **3**
    Summary of Investigations **3**
    Mathematics Background **4**
Content Connections to Other Units **9**
Planning for the Unit **10**
    Pacing Suggestions and Materials **10**
    Pacing for Block Scheduling **11**
    Vocabulary **11**
Program Resources **12**
    Components **12**
    Technology **12**
Assessment Summary **14**
    Ongoing Informal Assessment **14**
    Formal Assessment **14**
    Correlation to Standardized Tests **14**
Launching the Unit **15**
    Introducing Your Students to *Data About Us* **15**
    Using the Unit Opener **15**
    Introducing the Unit Project **15**
    Using the Mathematical Highlights **15**

> The Student Edition pages for the Unit Opener follow page 15.

Investigation 1 Looking at Data **16**

Mathematical and Problem-Solving Goals **16**
Summary of Problems **16**
1.1 Organizing and Interpreting Data **17**
1.2 Useful Statistics **21**
1.3 Experimenting With the Median **27**
1.4 Using Different Data Types **31**
1.5 Vertical Bar Graphs and Horizontal Bar Graphs **37**

The Student Edition pages for Investigation 1 follow page 40.

ACE Answers to Applications—Connections—Extensions **41**
Possible Answers to Mathematical Reflections **45**

Investigation 2 Using Graphs to Explore Data **46**

Mathematical and Problem-Solving Goals **46**
Summary of Problems **46**
2.1 Traveling to School: Making a Stem-and-Leaf Plot **47**
2.2 Jumping Rope: Comparing Distributions **53**
2.3 Relating Height to Arm Span: Making and Reading Coordinate Graphs **57**
2.4 Relating Travel Time to Distance: Using Coordinate Graphs to Find Relationships **63**

The Student Edition pages for Investigation 2 follow page 66.

ACE Answers to Applications—Connections—Extensions **67**
Possible Answers to Mathematical Reflections **71**

Investigation 3 **What Do We Mean by** *Mean*?. 73

Mathematical and Problem-Solving Goals. 73
Summary of Problems 73
3.1 Finding the Mean. 74
3.2 Data With the Same Mean 81
3.3 Using the Mean 87

The Student Edition pages for Investigation 3 follow page 90.

ACE Answers to Applications—Connections—Extensions 91
Possible Answers to Mathematical Reflections 93
Answers to Looking Back and Looking Ahead 94

Guide to the Unit Project. 96

The remaining Student Edition pages for the unit follow page 101.

Blackline Masters
  Labsheets for Students
    2.4 103
    2 **ACE** Exercise 15. 104
    Centimeter Grid Paper. 105
    At a Glance Teacher Form 106
Glossary 107
Index. 111
Acknowledgments 112

Data About Us
Statistics

Goals of the Unit

- Understand and use the process of data investigation: posing questions, collecting and analyzing data distributions, and making interpretations to answer questions

- Represent distributions of data using line plots, bar graphs, stem-and-leaf plots, and coordinate graphs

- Compute the mean, median, mode, and range of the data

- Distinguish between categorical data and numerical data and identify which graphs and statistics may be used to represent each kind of data

- Make informed decisions about which graph(s) and which of the measures of center (mean, median, or mode) and range may be used to describe a distribution of data

- Develop strategies for comparing distributions of data

Developing Students' Mathematical Habits

The overall goal of *Connected Mathematics* is to help students develop sound mathematical habits. Through their work in this and other data units, students learn important questions to ask themselves about any situation that involves data analysis, such as:

- What is the question being asked?

- How do I want to organize the data?

- Which representation is best for analyzing the distribution of the data?

- Do I want to determine a measure of center or the range of the data? If so, which statistic do I want to use and what will it tell me about the distribution of the data?

- How can I use graphs and statistics to describe a data distribution or to compare two data distributions in order to answer my original question?

Mathematics of the Unit

Overview

Exploring statistics as a process of data investigation involves a set of four interrelated components (Graham, 1987):

- Posing the question: formulating the key question(s) to explore and deciding what data to collect to address the question(s)

- Collecting the data: deciding how to collect the data as well as actually collecting it

- Analyzing the data: organizing, representing, summarizing, and describing the data and looking for patterns in the data

- Interpreting the results: predicting, comparing, and identifying relationships and using the results from the analyses to make decisions about the original question(s)

This dynamic process often involves moving back and forth among the four interconnected components. For example, collecting the data and, after some analysis, deciding to refine the question and gather additional data. It may involve spending time working within a single component. For example, creating several different representations of the data, some in earlier stages of the process and others at a later time, before selecting the representation(s) to be used for final presentation of the data.

In many of the problems, data are provided. We assume students have had experience collecting data as part of statistical investigations. If they have not, we encourage you to have your class collect their own data for some of the problems. The problems can be applied either to the data provided or to data collected by students.

Even if your students have already had experience collecting data, they may be interested in investigating data about their class. Students will feel empowered if they have the opportunity to use the process of data investigation to explore questions that are of interest to them. Keep in mind that collecting data is time-consuming, so carefully choose the problems for which you will have students generate data.

Summary of Investigations

Investigation 1
Looking at Data

This first investigation develops some introductory statistical techniques that will be used throughout *Data About Us*. It focuses on describing, interpreting, and comparing distributions. A discussion about the origin of names is used, providing an opportunity to integrate social studies. In addition, students consider lengths of names, and compare distributions of lengths of names from two data sets that are provided and their class's data. Students are introduced to or review the use of tables, line plots, and bar graphs to represent data; ways to describe the shape of a distribution; and the use of measures of center (the mode and median), spread, and range to characterize a distribution.

Students are also introduced to types of data, with a focus on categorical and numerical data. They consider two tables and graphs of data that relate to two questions, one that involves numerical data and one that involves categorical data. Finally, they experiment with using and making horizontal and vertical bar graphs.

Investigation 2
Using Graphs to Explore Data

This investigation first focuses on developing strategies for grouping and displaying data in intervals using stem-and-leaf plots. Data that are collected are often quite spread out or have a great deal of variability. A line plot or bar graph may not be very useful for displaying such data in order to see patterns in the distributions (e.g., clusters, gaps). Students need strategies for grouping and displaying data in equal intervals. The stem-and-leaf plot (or stem plot) is a useful tool for grouping data in intervals of 10, and it helps students see patterns in the data. Students use a stem-and-leaf plot to examine two given data sets. The first data set is about time and distance required for students in a particular class to travel to school. The second data set is about how many times each student in two different classes jumped rope without stopping.

Students then use coordinate graphs to display pairs of data. They begin by collecting data about the lengths of their arm spans and their heights. Using these data, they make a coordinate graph and sketch the $y = x$ line so they can discuss people who are above, on, or below the line and what this means in terms of the relationship between arm span and height (that is, are most people's arm span and height similar?). They return to the travel time and distance data set and look at a coordinate graph that shows a student's travel time paired with distance traveled in order to discuss whether there is a relationship between travel time and distance traveled (that is, does it take someone who travels farther more time to get to school?).

Investigation 3

What Do We Mean by *Mean*?

This investigation focuses on developing the concept of mean. The "average" number of people in the families of students in a class provides the setting. The notion of "evening out" or "balancing" the distribution at a point (the mean) located on the horizontal axis is modeled by using cubes and stick-on notes. These models support development of the algorithm for finding the mean: adding up all the numbers and dividing by the number of items.

Mathematics Background

In *Data About Us,* several big ideas about statistics are explored. On the next page is a concept map that provides some insights into the overall relationships among these and other important concepts. The shaded portions of the diagram and highlighted graph names are central statistical ideas that are emphasized in *Data About Us.*

Different Types of Data

Questions in real life often result in answers that involve one of two general kinds of data: categorical data or numerical data. Knowing the type of data helps us to determine the most appropriate measures of center and displays to use for the data.

Numerical Data

- We can collect data about family size and organize them by using frequencies of how many families have zero children, one child, two children, and so on.

- We can collect data about pulse rates and organize them using intervals by using frequencies of how many people have pulse rates in the intervals of 60 to 69 beats, 70 to 79 beats, and so on.

- We can collect data about height and organize them into intervals by using frequencies of how many people are from 40 to 44 inches tall, 45 to 49 inches tall, and so on.

- We can collect data about time spent sleeping in one day and organize them by frequencies of how many people slept 7 hours, $7\frac{1}{2}$ hours, 8 hours, and so on.

- We can collect data about responses to a question such as, "On a scale of 1 to 5 with 1 as 'low interest,' rate your interest in participating in the school's field day" and organize them by using frequencies of how many people indicated each of the ratings 1, 2, 3, 4, or 5.

- We can use the mean, median, mode, and range as summary statistics on any numerical data.

Categorical Data

- We can collect data about birth years and organize them by using frequencies of how many people were born in 1980, 1981, 1982, and so on.

- We can collect data about favorite type of book to read and organize them by using frequencies of how many people like mysteries, adventure stories, science fiction, and so on.

- We can collect data about hobbies and organize them by using frequencies of how many people collect stamps, build models, knit, and so on.

- Mode is the only summary statistic we can use on categorical data.

At times, categorical data seem to be organized like numerical data. A bar graph of birth months may employ numbers to represent months. For example, 1 is used for January, 2 is used for February, and 3 is used for March. However, we cannot perform numerical operations using months of the year, because months represented numerically are actually categories with a number label representing the category.

Doing Meaningful Statistics – Central Statistical Ideas for *Data About Us*

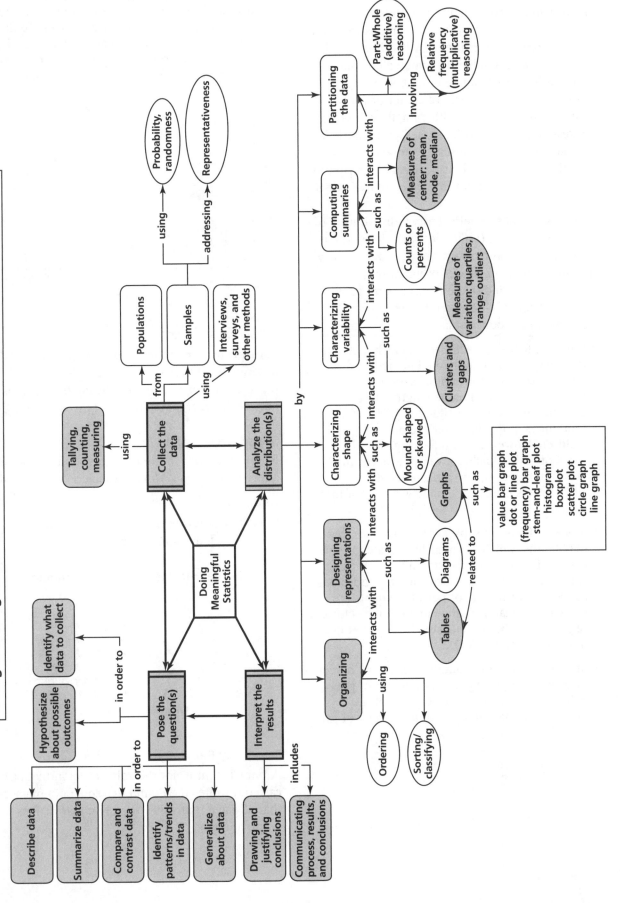

Distribution

The distribution of data refers to the way data occur in a data set. We often use graphs to help us see how data are distributed. A distribution (data as a whole versus individual data values) has characteristics that can be described using statistics such as measures of center or range.

When students work with data, they are often interested in the individual cases, particularly if the data are about themselves. However, statisticians like to look at the overall distribution of a data set and are not interested in individual cases.

We use graphs to help clarify a distribution of data. Distributions (unlike individual cases) have properties such as measures of central tendency (i.e., mean, median, mode) or variation (e.g., outliers, range) and shape (e.g., clusters, gaps).

There appear to be several general ways students think about data:

- Students focus on each data value. For example, they may focus on individual name lengths. They may not see that a group of cases may be related (e.g., several name lengths cluster around lengths of 8 to 10 letters). This kind of thinking is more characteristic of young children. However, when looking at outliers, a focus on individual data values is necessary. How might we explain a name length of 1,019 letters if this data value was part of the data set?

- Students focus on subsets of data values that may be the same or similar like a category or a cluster. This is easier for students when using categorical data (e.g., more students chose dogs as their favorite kind of pet). If students are using numerical data, they might notice clusters (e.g., the number of pets students have at home in the interval of 2 to 3).

- Students view all the data values as an "object" or distribution (see graph of number of pets below). Students look for features of the distribution that are not features of any of the

individual data values (e.g., shape, range, clusters). In looking at the distribution of the number of pets students have, we can see that data are clustered at one end with a kind of tail going off to the right that accounts for several cases in which students have more than six pets.

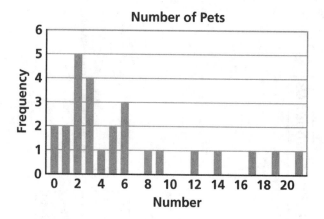

Data Reduction

Statisticians use the term "data reduction" to describe what they do when they use representations or statistics during the analysis part of the process of statistical investigation.

Standard Graphs

Representations in the K–12 curriculum that are addressed in *Data About Us* include the following:

Line Plot

Each case is represented as an "X" positioned over a labeled number line.

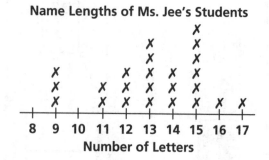

Frequency Bar Graph

A bar's height is not the value of an individual case but rather the number (frequency) of cases that all have that value. (See Number of Pets graph above.)

Stem-and-leaf plot

A plot that permits students to group data in intervals (usually by 10's). Stem plots are often introduced as a way to group data that have few repeated values and are spread out. In such situations, the use of line plots provides little information.

Student Travel Times to School

```
0 | 3 3 5 7 8 9
1 | 0 2 3 5 6 6 8 9
2 | 0 1 3 3 3 5 5 8 8
3 | 0 5
4 | 5
```

Key: 2 | 5 means 25 min

Coordinate graph

The relationship between two different variables is explored by plotting data values on a Cartesian coordinate system.

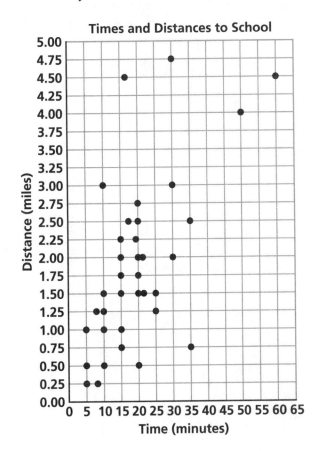

Times and Distances to School

As a central component of data analysis, graphs deserve special attention. Three components to graph comprehension that are useful are:

- *Reading the data* involves locating information from a graph to answer explicit questions. For example, "How many students have 12 letters in their names?"

- *Reading between the data* includes using clusters of information presented in a graph. For example, "How many students have more than 12 letters in their names?"

- *Reading beyond the data* involves extending, predicting, or inferring from data to answer questions. For example, "What is the typical number of letters in these students' names? If a new student joined our class, how many letters would you predict that student would have in his or her name?"

Once students create their graphs, they use them in the interpretation phase of the data-investigation process. This is when they (and you) need to ask questions about the graphs. The first two categories of questions, reading the data and reading between the data, are basic to understanding graphs. However, it is reading beyond the data that helps students to develop higher-level thinking skills such as inference and justification.

Measures of Center

We assume mode and median have been addressed during experiences with data analysis in the elementary grades. We also assume that mean may be a relatively new concept. We emphasize the fair share (or evening out) interpretation of mean (average) in *Data About Us*. For example, Ossie has two people in his family. Leon and Gary each have three people in their families. Ruth has four people in her family. Paul and Arlene each have six people. What is the average (mean) number people in these six households?

Before:

Ossie	2 people
Leon	3 people
Gary	3 people
Ruth	4 people
Paul	6 people
Arlene	6 people
Total	24 people

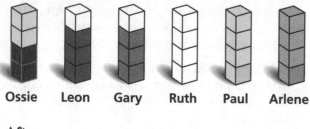

| Ossie | Leon | Gary | Ruth | Paul | Arlene |

After:

Ossie	4 people
Leon	4 people
Gary	4 people
Ruth	4 people
Paul	4 people
Arlene	4 people
Total	24 people

Mode is the value that occurs with greatest frequency in a set of data.

Median is the value that marks the location that separates an ordered set of data into two equal-sized groups, with the same number of values before the median and after the median.

Although there is one median in a set of data, there may be more than one mode.

In a data set with an even number of values, where the two middle values differ by more than one, the median is the midpoint between these values. For example, the median for the data set 3, 4, 4, 7, 8, 9 is $5\frac{1}{2}$, the number that is the midpoint between 4 and 7. If the two middle values are the same number, the median is the value of that number. For example, for the data set 3, 4, 5, 5, 7, 8, the median falls between the two 5's, so the median is 5.

Measures of Variation

Measures of variation establish the degree of variability or scatter of the individual data values and their deviations from (or differences from) the measures of center. In *Data About Us*, students use *range* as one measure of variation. Range is the difference between the least and the greatest data values. In addition, students are encouraged to talk about where data cluster and where there are "holes" in the data as further ways to comment about variation.

Covariation

Covariation is a way of characterizing a kind of relationship between two variables. It means that information about values from one variable helps us to understand and explain or predict values of the other variable. In *Data About Us*, students are asked to think about whether changes in one variable (e.g., time traveled to school) might be related to changes in another variable (e.g., distance traveled to school). The primary goal for this unit is to review using a coordinate graph to represent data. More formal work with covariation continues in the other data units.

Big Idea	Prior Work	Future Work
Collecting and organizing categorical and numerical data	Analyzing and classifying counting numbers (*Prime Time, Bits and Piece II, Covering and Surrounding, Bits and Pieces III, How Likely Is It?*)	Gathering and organizing data collected from conducting experiments or trials of games (*What Do You Expect?, Data Distributions, Samples and Populations*)
Representing data with line plots, bar graphs, coordinate graphs, and stem-and-leaf plots	Representing the number of proper factors of a counting number (*Prime Time*), graphing rectangle lengths and widths with constant perimeter or constant area (*Covering and Surrounding*)	Representing data to aid with statistical analysis (*Data Distributions, Samples and Populations*); expanding the use of coordinate grids to include negative coordinates (*Accentuate the Negative; Moving Straight Ahead; Thinking With Mathematical Models; Frogs, Fleas, and Painted Cubes; Kaleidoscopes, Hubcaps, and Mirrors; Say It With Symbols; The Shapes of Algebra*)
Finding measures of center	Ordering numbers from least to greatest, counting (elementary school, *Bits and Pieces I, Bits and Pieces III*)	Using measures of center to make inferences and predictions about events or populations (*Data Distributions, Samples and Populations*)
Finding measures of variation of a set of data	Comparing, counting, and ordering numbers (elementary school), spread of measures (*Bits and Pieces III*)	Using the "variation" or "shape" of a data set to make judgments about the accuracy and reliability of the data and to make inferences and predictions about the group to which the data pertains (*Data Distributions, Samples and Populations*)
Calculating the mean	Using arithmetic operations (especially addition and division); learning the meaning of rational numbers (elementary school, *Bits and Pieces III*)	Developing further understanding about what the mean does and does not measure about a data set; using the mean together with other measures to make predictions and inferences from data (*Data Distributions, Samples and Populations*)

Planning for the Unit

Pacing Suggestions and Materials

Investigations and Assessments	Pacing 45–50 min. classes	Materials for Students	Materials for Teachers
1 Looking at Data	6 days (if collecting own data, add 2 days)	Class list of students (optional), stick-on notes (optional), centimeter grid paper, graph paper, scissors, index cards (20 per group)	Transparencies 1.1A, 1.1B, 1.2A, 1.2B, 1.3, 1.4A–C, 1.5A, 1.5B; class lists of students by first and last name (optional); stick-on notes; gridded chart paper (optional)
Mathematical Reflections	$\frac{1}{2}$ day		
Assessment: Check Up 1	$\frac{1}{2}$ day		
2 Using Graphs to Explore Data	$4\frac{1}{2}$ days (if collecting own data, add 2 days)	Graph paper, yardsticks (or meter sticks or tape measures), string (optional), Labsheets 2.4 and 2ACE Exercise 15	Transparencies 2.1A–C, 2.2, 2.3A, 2.3B, 2.4; large grid paper (optional); colored stick-on dots (optional); local street map (optional)
Mathematical Reflections	$\frac{1}{2}$ day		
Assessment: Partner Quiz	1 day		
3 What Do We Mean by *Mean*?	$3\frac{1}{2}$ days	Cubes (10 each of 6 different colors per group), stick-on notes, large sheets of unlined paper	Transparencies 3.1A, 3.1B, 3.2A, 3.2B, 3.3A, 3.3B; cubes (10 each of 6 different colors); stick-on notes
Mathematical Reflections	$\frac{1}{2}$ day		
Looking Back and Looking Ahead	$\frac{1}{2}$ day		
Assessment: Unit Project	Take Home		
Assessment: Self Assessment	1 day		
Assessment: Unit Test	1 day		

	Total Time $19\frac{1}{2}$ days	Materials for Use in All Investigations	
For detailed pacing for Problems within each Investigation, see the Suggested Pacing at the beginning of each Investigation.		Calculators, blank transparencies and transparency markers (optional), student notebooks	Blank transparencies and transparency markers (optional)
For pacing with block scheduling, see next page.			

Pacing for Block Scheduling (90-minute class periods)

Investigation	Suggested Pacing	Investigation	Suggested Pacing	Investigation	Suggested Pacing
Investigation 1	**4 days**	**Investigation 2**	**3 days**	**Investigation 3**	**$2\frac{1}{2}$ days**
Problem 1.1	1 day	Problem 2.1	$\frac{1}{2}$ day	Problem 3.1	1 day
Problem 1.2	1 day	Problem 2.2	$\frac{1}{2}$ day	Problem 3.2	$\frac{1}{2}$ day
Problem 1.3	$\frac{1}{2}$ day	Problem 2.3	1 day	Problem 3.3	$\frac{1}{2}$ day
Problem 1.4	$\frac{1}{2}$ day	Problem 2.4	$\frac{1}{2}$ day	Math Reflections	$\frac{1}{2}$ day
Problem 1.5	$\frac{1}{2}$ day	Math Reflections	$\frac{1}{2}$ day		
Math Reflections	$\frac{1}{2}$ day				

Vocabulary

Essential Terms Developed in This Unit	Useful Terms Referenced in This Unit	Terms Developed in Previous Units
bar graph	average	fraction
categorical data	back-to-back stem plot	decimal
coordinate graph	compare	percent
line plot	data	
mean	distribution	
median	double bar graph	
mode	household	
numerical data	measures of centers	
outlier	predict, prediction	
range	scale	
stem-and-leaf plot (stem plot)	stacked bar graph	
x-axis	survey	
y-axis	table	

Go Online
PHSchool.com
For: Teacher Resources
Web Code: amk-5500

Components

Use the chart below to quickly see which components are available for each Investigation.

Investigation	Labsheets	Additional Practice	Transparencies		Formal Assessment		Assessment Options	
			Problem	Summary	Check Up	Partner Quiz	Multiple-Choice	Question Bank
1		✔	1.1A, 1.1B, 1.2A, 1.2B, 1.3, 1.4A–C, 1.5A, 1.5B		✔		✔	✔
2	2.4, 2ACE Exercise 15	✔	2.1A–C, 2.2, 2.3A, 2.3B, 2.4			✔	✔	✔
3		✔	3.1A, 3.1B, 3.2A, 3.2B, 3.3A, 3.3B				✔	✔
Unit Project								
For the Unit		*ExamView* CD-ROM, Web site			Unit Test, Unit Project, Notebook Check, Self Assessment		Multiple-Choice, Question Bank, *ExamView* CD-ROM	

Also Available for Use With This Unit

- Parent Guide: take-home letter for the unit
- Implementing CMP
- Spanish Assessment Resources
- Additional online and technology resources

Technology

The Use of Calculators

Connected Mathematics was developed with the belief that calculators should be available and that students should learn when their use is appropriate. For this reason, we do not designate specific problems as "calculator problems." The calculations in *Data About Us* involve only simple arithmetic, so nonscientific calculators are adequate. The unit may be pursued without access to software; however, if appropriate software is available, we encourage you to introduce your students to its use as part of this unit's activities. Use of such software may well improve students' understanding of the structure of graphs and will certainly promote their exploration of different graphs.

Student Interactivity CD-ROM

Includes interactive activities to enhance the learning in the Problems within Investigations.

Links to additional software activities that allow students to experiment with making different distributions that match specific conditions such as: 10 data items with a mean of 6 and a median of 5 are available through Web Code amk-5500.

PHSchool.com

For Students Multiple-choice practice with instant feedback, updated data sources, Tinkerplots software for data analysis.

For Teachers Downloadable forms for Substitute Teachers, professional development, curriculum support, and more.

See also www.math.msu.edu/cmp for more resources for both teachers and students.

ExamView® CD-ROM

Create multiple versions of practice sheets and tests for course objectives and standardized tests. Includes dynamic questions, online testing, student reports, and all test and practice items in Spanish. Also includes all items in the Assessment Resources and Additional Practice.

Teacher Express™ CD-ROM

Includes a lesson planning tool, the Teacher's Guide pages, and all the teaching resources.

LessonLab Online Courses

LessonLab offers comprehensive, facilitated professional development designed to help teachers implement CMP2 and improve student achievement. To learn more, please visit PHSchool.com/cmp2.

Assessment Summary

Ongoing Informal Assessment

Embedded in the Student Unit

Problems Use students' work from the Problems to informally check student understanding.

ACE exercises Use ACE exercises for homework assignments to assess student understanding.

Mathematical Reflections Have students summarize their learning at the end of each Investigation.

Looking Back and Looking Ahead At the end of the unit, use the first two sections to allow students to show what they know about the unit.

Additional Resources

Teacher's Guide Use the Check for Understanding feature of some Summaries and the probing questions that appear in the *Launch, Explore,* or *Summarize* sections of all Investigations to check student understanding.

Self Assessment

Notebook Check Students use this tool to organize and check their notebooks before giving them to their teacher. Located in *Assessment Resources*.

Self Assessment At the end of the unit, students reflect on and provide examples of what they learned. Located in *Assessment Resources*.

Formal Assessment

Choose the assessment materials that are appropriate for your students.

Assessment	For Use After	Focus	Student Work
Check Up 1	Invest. 1	Skills	Individual
Partner Quiz	Invest. 2	Rich problems	Pair
Unit Test	The Unit	Skills, rich problems	Individual
Unit Project	The Unit	Rich problems	Group or Individual

Additional Resources

Multiple-Choice Items Use these items for home-work, review, a quiz, or add them to the Unit Test.

Question Bank Choose from these questions for homework, review, or replacements for Quiz, Check Up, or Unit Test questions.

Additional Practice Choose practice exercises for each investigation for homework, review, or formal assessments.

ExamView **CD-ROM** Create practice sheets, review quizzes, and tests with this dynamic software. Give online tests and receive student progress reports. (All test items are also available in Spanish.)

Spanish Assessment Resources

Includes Partner Quizzes, Check Ups, Unit Test, Multiple-Choice Items, Question Bank, Notebook Check, and Self Assessment. Plus, the *ExamView* CD-ROM has all test items in Spanish.

Correlation to Standardized Tests

Investigation	NAEP	Terra Nova				Local Test
		CAT6	CTBS	ITBS	SAT10	
1 Looking at Data	D1a, D1b, D1c, D1d, D1e, D2a, D2b, D2c, D2d	✔	✔	✔	✔	
2 Using Graphs to Explore Data	D1a, D1b, D1c, D1d, D1e, D2a, D2b, D2c, D2d	✔			✔	
3 What Do We Mean by *Mean*?	D1a, D1c, D2a, D2b, D2c, D2d	✔	✔	✔	✔	

NAEP National Assessment of Educational Progress

CAT6/Terra Nova California Achievement Test, 6th Ed.
CTBS/Terra Nova Comprehensive Test of Basic Skills

ITBS Iowa Test of Basic Skills, Form M
SAT10 Stanford Achievement Test, 10th Ed.

Introducing Your Students to *Data About Us*

One way to introduce *Data About Us* is to have a class discussion about the "typical" middle school student. Ask students what they think the word *typical* means. Then ask them what they think are some characteristics of a typical middle school student. What is the typical height? The typical favorite musical group? The typical number of siblings?

Discuss whether typical characteristics of your class would be typical of a class in another part of town, another state, or another country. For example, would the typical favorite food for students in your class be the same as the typical favorite food for a middle school class in Japan?

Using the Unit Opener

Discuss the questions posed on the opening page of the Student Edition, which are designed to start students thinking about the kinds of questions and mathematics in the unit. Don't look for "correct" answers at this time. Do, however, present an opportunity for the class to discuss the questions and to start to think about what is needed to answer them. You may want to revisit these questions as students learn the mathematical ideas and techniques necessary to find the answers.

Problems in contexts are used to help students informally reason about the mathematics of the unit. The problems are deliberately sequenced to develop understanding of concepts and skills.

Introducing the Unit Project

An optional assessment item for *Data About Us* is the *Is Anyone Typical?* project. Explain that, in this unit, students will gather and analyze data to try to find out some typical characteristics of their classmates. Have students suggest some things they would like to know about their classmates. Then, have them suggest questions they could ask to find out this information.

Throughout the unit, students are reminded to use the concepts they are learning to write more questions they might ask about their classmates. At the end of the unit, students are asked to gather and analyze class data in order to answer the question: Is anyone typical?

You may want to set aside a few minutes of class time for students to write their questions. Some teachers have found it useful to have students designate one or two "special data pages" in their notebooks to record information about their questions.

See the Guide to the Unit Project section on page 96 for more information about assigning and assessing the project. There you will find a rubric and samples of student projects. Each sample is followed by a teacher's comments about assessing the project.

Using the Mathematical Highlights

The Mathematical Highlights page in the Student Edition provides information to students, parents, and other family members. It gives students a preview of the mathematics and some of the overarching questions that they should ask themselves while studying *Data About Us*.

As they work through the unit, students can refer back to the Mathematical Highlights page to review what they have learned and to preview what is still to come. This page also tells students' families what mathematical ideas and activities will be covered as the class works through *Data About Us*.

Data About Us

Statistics

Glenda Lappan
James T. Fey
William M. Fitzgerald
Susan N. Friel
Elizabeth Difanis Phillips

Boston, Massachusetts · Glenview, Illinois · Shoreview, Minnesota · Upper Saddle River, New Jersey

Notes _____

_____

_____

_____

Data About Us

What is the greatest number of pets owned by students in your class? How can you find out?

Suppose two classes competed in a jump-rope contest. They recorded the number of jumps for each student. How would you determine which class did better?

A group of students collected data on the number of movies they watched last month. How would you find out the "typical" number of movies watched?

2   Data About Us

Notes _____

_____

_____

_____

very 10 years the United States government conducts a *census*, or survey, of every household in the country. The census gathers information about many things including education, employment, and income. Because people are naturally curious about themselves and others, many people are interested in information from the census. Of course, collecting data from every household in the United States is a huge task.

You often hear people making statements about the results of surveys. For example, what does it mean when reports say the average middle-school student has four people in his or her family, or watches three hours of television on a weekday?

In *Data About Us,* you will learn to collect and analyze data for situations similar to those on the previous page. You will also learn to use your results to describe people and their characteristics.

Notes _____

_____

_____

_____

Mathematical Highlights

In *Data About Us*, you will explore ways of collecting, organizing, displaying, and analyzing data.

You will learn how to

- Conduct data investigations by posing questions, collecting and analyzing data, and making interpretations to answer questions
- Represent distributions of data using line plots, bar graphs, stem-and-leaf plots, and coordinate graphs
- Compute the mean, median, mode, or range of the data
- Distinguish between categorical data and numerical data and identify which graphs and statistics may be used to represent each kind of data
- Choose the most appropriate statistical measures (mean, median, mode, range, etc.) to describe a distribution of data
- Develop strategies for comparing distributions of data

As you work on problems in this unit, ask yourself questions about situations that involve data analysis:

What is the question being asked?

What organization of the data can help me analyze the data?

What statistical measures will provide useful information about the distribution of data?

What will statistical measures tell me about the distribution of the data?

How can I use graphs and statistics to describe a data distribution or to compare two data distributions in order to answer my original question?

4 Data About Us

Notes _____

_____

_____

_____

Unit Project

Is Anyone Typical?

What are the characteristics of a typical middle-school student? Who is interested in knowing these characteristics? Does a typical middle-school student really exist? As you proceed through this unit, you will identify some "typical" facts about your classmates, such as these:

- The typical number of letters in a student's full name
- The typical number of people in a student's household
- The typical height of a student

When you have completed the investigations in *Data About Us,* you will carry out a statistical investigation to answer this question:

What are some of the characteristics of a typical middle-school student?

These characteristics may include

- Physical characteristics (for example, age, height, or eye color)
- Family and home characteristics (for example, number of brothers and sisters or number of MP3 players)
- Behaviors (for example, hobbies or number of hours spent watching television)
- Preferences, opinions, or attitudes (for example, favorite musical group, or choice for class president)

As you study this unit, make and improve your plans for your project. Keep in mind that a statistical investigation involves posing questions, collecting data, analyzing data, and interpreting the results of the analysis. As you work through each investigation, think about how you might use what you are learning to help you with your project.

Notes _____

_____

_____

_____

Investigation 1 Looking at Data

Mathematical and Problem-Solving Goals

- Describe data distributions
- Use tables, line plots, and bar graphs to display data distributions
- Use mode, median, how the data vary from the least to the greatest values, and range to describe what is typical about a data distribution
- Recognize how the median, as a measure of center, responds to changes in the number and magnitude of data values
- Identify whether data are categorical or numerical
- Understand how mode, median, and range relate to numerical and categorical data
- Distinguish between and answer questions using vertical and horizontal bar graphs

Summary of Problems

Problem 1.1 Organizing and Interpreting Data

Students review (or learn) the structure and use of line plots and bar graphs. In addition, students begin to compare distributions.

Problem 1.2 Useful Statistics

Students fold paper strips to see that the median divides a data set in half. In addition, students create data distributions with a given range, mode, and median to recognize the parts that the mode, range, and median play in describing and comparing graphs.

Problem 1.3 Experimenting With the Median

Students investigate how the median of a data set changes as values are added or removed.

Problem 1.4 Using Different Data Types

Students investigate categorical and numerical data collected about pets. They determine whether questions can be answered using the data represented by tables and graphs, or whether more information is required.

Problem 1.5 Vertical Bar Graphs and Horizontal Bar Graphs

Students make and read bar graphs that are displayed vertically and bar graphs that are displayed horizontally.

Mathematics Background

For background on different types of data, distribution, and data reduction, see pages 4–8.

	Suggested Pacing	Materials for Students	Materials for Teachers	ACE Assignments
All	$6\frac{1}{2}$ days	Calculators, blank transparencies and transparency markers (optional), student notebooks	Blank transparencies and transparency markers (optional)	
1.1	$1\frac{1}{2}$ days	Class list of students (optional)	Transparencies 1.1A, 1.1B, class list of students by first and last name (optional)	1, 22–25
1.2	$1\frac{1}{2}$ days	Stick-on notes (optional), centimeter grid paper, graph paper, scissors	Transparencies 1.2A, 1.2B	2–12, 26–28
1.3	1 day	Index cards (20 per group)	Transparency 1.3	13, 29, 30
1.4	1 day		Transparencies 1.4A–C	14–20, 31, 32, 40–43
1.5	1 day		Transparencies 1.5A, 1.5B	21, 33–39
MR	$\frac{1}{2}$ day			

1.1 Organizing and Interpreting Data

Goals

- Describe data distributions
- Use line plots and bar graphs to display data distributions

In this problem, students compare two different representations, a line plot and a bar graph, of the same data set to review (or learn) the structure and use of these two representations. In addition, students collect and display data about the numbers of letters in their names, and compare it to the given class's data. While comparing the representations of the data sets, students begin describing data distributions.

Students can revisit the data in Problem 1.1 as they encounter new ways of making sense of data.

Launch 1.1

Suggested Question Use the introduction to the problem to ask how students were named.

- *Do you know anything interesting about how you were named or about the history behind your family's name?*

Then use the Getting Ready to determine the knowledge students have about collecting, organizing, and representing data. Students need to think about the process of statistical investigation whether they are collecting their own data or are using data provided for them. When students are involved in a problem in which they do their own data collection, following through with the process of statistical investigation is a natural part of the task. When students are analyzing a data set that they have not collected, it is important to help them first understand the data. You can do this by having students ask themselves the same kinds of questions they would ask if they were carrying out the data-collection process themselves. Questions such as these are helpful:

- What question was asked that resulted in these data being collected?
- How do you think the data were collected?
- Why are these data represented using this kind of graph?

- What are ways to describe the data distribution?

Explain to the students how we often use graphs to help us see how data are distributed. Make a distinction between a distribution (a picture of the data as a whole) and individual data values. Include how a distribution has characteristics that can be described using statistics such as measures of center or variation. You should also discuss with your students what the word *typical* means.

Explain to students:

- *You will be comparing a graph representing name lengths of a given class to a graph of our own class's name lengths. As you work on the graphs, think about what is the typical number of letters in the name of a student in our class.*

The data given counted first and last names. Part of the process of statistical investigation involves determining exactly what data need to be collected, so it is important that the class understand the choice to use only first and last names.

Suggested Questions You may ask some of these questions:

- *Do you use nicknames or full first names?*
- *Does the hyphen in a name such as Clarke-Peterson or Mai-Lin count as a letter?*

Because research has shown that students do not automatically "translate across representations," students may not initially view the line plot and the bar graph as comparable representations and may not recognize when a line plot and a bar graph display identical information. This problem provides an opportunity for you to assess and reinforce students' understanding.

Show Transparency 1.1B as students look at Problem 1.1 in their book, then read Problem 1.1 aloud.

Suggested Questions Ask the class to explain how they think the line plot and the bar graph were made.

- *What do the X's on the line plot represent?* (each student with the number of letters in their name on which the X is stacked)

- *What do the bars on the bar graph represent?* (total of the students with the number of letters in their name on which the bar is situated)

- *What does each axis represent?* (The horizontal axis represents the number of letters in students' names, and the vertical axis represents the number of students with the given number of letters in their name.)

- *How is the X that is above 17 in the line plot represented in the bar graph?* (It has a bar that aligns with a frequency of one.)

Have students work in pairs for Questions A–D. You might want to summarize Questions A–D before you launch Questions E and F.

For Question E, have students work in small groups to collect the data, or gather the data as a class. If you collect the data as a class by recording the counts on the board or at the overhead, be sure to collect it in a way that does not automatically organize it. For example, students can take turns calling out the number of letters in their names while you record each number on the board.

Once the data are collected, have students choose a way to organize and represent the data.

Explore 1.1

For Questions A–D, ask questions as you circulate to help keep students focused on the problem.

For Question C, help students move beyond counting the X's on the line plot.

Suggested Questions If they use only the line plot to answer Question C, ask:

- *How could you find the total number of letters in all their names using the bar graph?* (Add the frequency for each bar.)

For those students struggling with Question D, you might ask:

- *What does it mean to have the most letters in a name versus the most frequent number of letters in a name?* (Possible answer: A name length can be the longest, but it may not represent the name length occurring most frequently, for example, 17 in Ms. Jee's class.)

- *What is the name length that occurred with the greatest frequency in Ms. Jee's class?* (15)

- *How did you figure that out?* (Possible answer: I looked at the number of letters that had the highest bar on the graph.)

If students are confused with Questions E and F, you may get them started by asking:

- *How do you think we should organize this information? Suppose you wanted to tell another class about the name lengths of students in our class. It would be helpful to organize and display the data so you can see patterns and determine a typical name length.*

In comparing the two data distributions, you may want to encourage students to look at where the data cluster, at the high and low values, and at any unusual name lengths. These may be "talking points" for saying how the two distributions are similar or different from one another.

Summarize 1.1

Begin the summary by discussing the answers to the problem. Spend some time discussing Questions C and D. These questions will help students focus on important features of the graphs. They may have greater difficulty than you might imagine with these kinds of questions.

For Questions E and F, ask two or three groups to show and explain their work, including the groups you noticed that had found good ways to display the data. Use Question F to determine what students know about describing distributions with measures of center. Do not push them to use these statistics at this point because they will work with these statistics in the next investigation.

Suggested Question After the students have looked at each other's graphs, ask:

- *Looking at the graphs, what do you think is the typical name length for a middle school student? Explain your thinking.*

Students are actually addressing this question using two different distributions. You might want to focus on each distribution separately. The students will probably use a variety of ways to answer the question. See if they mention, for example, the mean or the median.

1.1 Organizing and Interpreting Data

Mathematical Goals

- Describe data distributions
- Use line plots and bar graphs to display data distributions

Launch

Engage students in a brief discussion of names.

- *Do you know anything interesting about how you were named or about the history behind your family's name?*

Use the Getting Ready to determine students' knowledge about collecting, organizing, and representing data. Have students determine exactly what they consider to be a full name.

- *Do you use nicknames or full first names?*

Show Transparency 1.1B, and then read Problem 1.1 aloud.

- *What do the X's on the line plot represent?*
- *What do the bars on the bar graph represent?*
- *What does each axis represent?*
- *How is the X above 17 in the line plot represented in the bar graph?*

Students work in pairs for Questions A–D, and in small groups for Question E. Summarize Questions A–D before you launch Questions E and F. Collect data and let students choose its organization and representation.

Materials

- Transparencies 1.1A and 1.1B
- Class list of students by first and last name (optional)

Vocabulary

- line plot
- bar graph

Explore

For Question C, help students move beyond counting X's on the line plot.

- *How could you find out the total number of letters in all their names using the bar graph?*

For those students struggling with Question D, you might ask:

- *What does it mean to have the most letters in a name versus the most frequent number of letters in a name?*
- *What is the name length that occurred with the greatest frequency in Ms. Jee's class? How did you figure that out?*

For Questions E and F, if students are confused, get them started by asking:

- *How do you think we should organize this information? Suppose you wanted to tell another class about our class's name lengths. It would be helpful to organize and display the data so you can see patterns and determine a typical name length.*

Encourage students to look at where the data cluster, at the high and low values, and at any unusual name lengths.

Spend time discussing Questions C and D. For Questions E and F, give time to show and explain work. After students look at each other's graphs, ask:

- *Looking at the graphs, what do you think is the typical name length for a middle school student? Explain your thinking.*

If you focus on the distributions separately the students may answer the question in different ways. See if they mention, for example, the mean or the median. In focusing on both distributions together, put both sets of data on one graph and discuss what is typical.

Materials
- Student notebooks

ACE Assignment Guide for Problem 1.1

Differentiated
Instruction
Solutions for All Learners

Core 1, 22–25

Adapted For suggestions about adapting ACE exercises, see the CMP *Special Needs Handbook.*

Answers to Problem 1.1

A. Possible answers: There is one peak at a name length of 15 letters. The shortest name is 9 letters, and the longest name is 17 letters. Only two of the names are longer than 15 letters. Most of the name lengths cluster in the interval of 12–15 letters.

B. Possible answers: Both graphs have titles and their axes are labeled. They have similar horizontal scales, which show the possible name lengths. The line plot does not have a vertical scale; the frequency of a particular name length is indicated by the number of X's above that number. The bar graph has a vertical scale; the frequency of a particular name length is indicated by the height of the bar over that number.

C. For the bar graph, you could multiply the height of each bar by the name length each bar represents. For example, three people have nine letters in their name, so the bar over the 9 accounts for 9 × 3, or 27, letters. Add the results for each bar to find the total number of letters. For the line plot, you could multiply the number of X's over each name length by that name length and add the results.

D. The height of a bar does not represent a name length; it represents the number of people with a particular name length. Because Fahimeh is the only student who has a name with 17 letters, the bar over the 17 has a height of 1.

E. Answers will vary.

F. Answers will vary. Students may compare the distributions by focusing on their clusters or gaps. Although it is not expected, some may use statistical descriptors such as range, mean, mode, or median.

1.2 Useful Statistics

Goals

- Use mode, median, how data vary from the least to the greatest values, and range to describe what is typical about a data distribution

- Use tables and line plots to display data distributions

In this section, the median is introduced as a measure of the center of a distribution.

Mathematics Background

For background on measures of center and measures of spread, see pages 7 and 8.

Launch 1.2

Suggested Questions You can begin by asking students what the word median means to them.

- *When you hear the word "median," what do you think of?* (Many students will say, "The strip down the middle of a road.")

- *In this problem you will find out what the median and the mode mean in a mathematical sense. You will also learn about range and the variation shown by the least and greatest data values.*

You can start by reviewing both the mode and range. It is expected that students have encountered these statistics in early work in elementary school.

- *When you describe a set of data, it is helpful to give the value that occurs most often. Look back at the data for Ms. Jee's class. Which name length occurs most often?* (A name length of 15 letters occurs most often.)

- *The value that occurs most often in a set of data is called the mode. The mode for Ms. Jee's class data is 15 letters.*

- *How can you find the mode by looking at a line plot or a bar graph?* (On a line graph, the mode has the highest stack of X's. On a bar graph, the mode has the tallest bar.)

- *Notice that the shortest name in Ms. Jee's class has 9 letters, and the longest name has 17 letters. The data vary from the least value to the greatest value. Ms. Jee's class data vary from 9 letters to 17 letters. The range of a data set is the difference between the greatest value and least value. The range of Ms. Jee's class data is 8 (17 − 9).*

Be careful how students word their descriptions of the mode. For example, for Ms. Jee's class, the mode is 15 letters. Students may say that "most students have 15 letters in their names." This is not true. There are 24 students in the data set, and only 6 of the students have 15 letters in their names. The mode is the name length that occurs most frequently.

- *The median is another way to describe what is typical, because it is the middle point of a set of data.*

Have students refer to the data for Problem 1.2 in their books, or display Transparencies 1.2A and 1.2B.

- *This table and the line plot show name-length data for Mr. Gray's class.*

- *We want to find the median, or middle value, for these data. The median separates the data so that the same number of data values are before this value and after this value. To find the median, we must first order the data from least to greatest.*

Write each name length on a large stick-on note, and display the lengths in the order they occur in the table.

Work with the class to rearrange the name lengths in order from least to greatest.

Have students work in pairs for Problem 1.2.

After you have ordered the data as a class, have students work on Questions A and B. Then move to Question C that shows a distribution for pet data. This line plot raises the issue of what effect a missing value has on the median. Students see that the median does not have to match a value for the length of one of the pet names.

For Question D, students are given the number of values in a data set and the mode and spread of the values. They must work backwards from this information to create a possible distribution. If students are having trouble, read aloud the description of the hypothetical class given in Question D.

Suggested Questions

- *What facts do we know about this class of students?* (mode is 12 letters; median is 12 letters; data vary from 8 to 16 letters; range is 8 letters.)

- *How can we use this information to find a set of name lengths for this class?* (Students may suggest beginning with names that have 8 and 16 letters, respectively, and then creating a few names with 12 letters.)

- *Is there more than one possible set of name lengths that fits this description? Why or why not?* (Students should see that there are many data sets that fit the description given. Each possible data set will have 15 values between (and including) 8 and 16, and the value 12 must occur with the greatest frequency.)

For Question D, each pair of students should create a line plot that meets the criteria of the problem and can be posted for the rest of the class to see. You may want to have students make their line plots on large sheets of paper, using stick-on notes instead of X's, or with transparencies and transparency markers that can easily be erased and redrawn.

For Questions A and B, to help students understand the median, you may want to create your own large strips of ordered data values, one strip for the original 21 values and the other for the 22 values. In each case, draw a dark line to indicate the median. You could use gridded chart paper (available in office supply stores). Hold up the strip with 21 values.

- *For the strip of 21 values, the fold occurred on a 12. The same number of data values were before the fold and after the fold. We say that the median name length for this set of names is 12 letters.*

Now hold up the strip of 22 values.

- *For the strip of 22 values, the fold did not occur on a number. It occurred between 12 and 13. In a case like this, where there is an even number of values, we define the median as the number halfway between the two middle values. In this case, the median name length is $12\frac{1}{2}$.*

Suggested Questions Now, direct students to the table and graph of the original data.

- *Look back at the original data set and line plot. The median name length is 12 letters. Where is this located on the line plot?* (It is located as a marker at the "12" on the line plot. Notice that there are several data values that match the median's value.)

- *Earlier we found a different measure of center called the mode. How does the median compare with the mode in this data set?* (The data set has two modes, 11 letters and 12 letters. The median, 12 letters, is the same as one of the modes.)

- *After we add the data for Suzanne Mannerstrale, how does the median compare with the mode?* (The median, $12\frac{1}{2}$ letters, is no longer the same as either of the modes. You may want to point out that, while the mode is always a value in the data set, the median may not be. In this case, the median $12\frac{1}{2}$ is not even a possible value for a name length.)

- *What would happen to the median and the mode if another student joined the class with a name length of 11 letters?* (The median would be 12 letters, and the mode would be 11 letters.)

- *Can the median have the same value as the mode?* (The two measures of center can have the same value.)

- *If we had a lot of data values, folding a strip of paper to find the median would be an inefficient strategy. Can you think of another way to find the median?* (Students may have several valid suggestions. One possibility is to make an ordered list of the name lengths and count in from the ends, pairing one length from the "small" end with one length from the "large" end until you work your way to the middle. Another possibility is to make an ordered list of the name lengths. If there is an even number of data values, divide the number of values in half. The result will be a whole number. Count that many values from one end of the data. The median will be the midpoint between the number you land on and the next number. If there are an odd number of data values, divide the number of values in half. The result will be a fraction. Round the fraction to the next whole number, and count over that many values from one end of the data. The number you land on will be the value of the median.)

- *Now look at Question C. What is the median?* (The median is 10.)

For Question D, the goal is not for students to determine all possible answers, but to realize that many solutions are possible. The criteria provide some constraints on the shape of the data, but the remaining information can be chosen in many different ways to create a data set.

Have students display their line plots. They will have created a variety of data sets of name lengths. Any graph that satisfies the conditions of the problem is acceptable.

Suggested Questions Have students compare their graphs by asking questions like these:

- *Look at the different line plots that were made. How are they alike?* (All graphs should show 15 X's, a mode of 12 letters, and a spread from 8 to 16 letters.)

- *How are the line plots different?* (The shapes of the displays may look very different from one another.)

- *Why are different displays possible?* (Not all the necessary information is provided, so you can find different displays that fit the given information.)

Mathematical Goals

- Use mode, median, how data vary from the least to the greatest values, and range to describe what is typical about a data distribution
- Use tables and line plots to display data distributions

Launch

You can begin by asking students what the word median means to them.

- *When you hear the word "median," what do you think of?*
- *In this problem you will find out what the median and the mode mean in a mathematical sense. You will also learn about range and spread.*

Review both the mode and range using Ms. Jee's data.

Have students refer to the data for Problem 1.2, or display Transparencies 1.2A and 1.2B.

- *We want to find the median, or middle value, for these data. The median separates the data so that the same number of data values are before this value and after this value. To find the median, we must first order the data from least to greatest.*

Write each name length on a large stick-on note, and display the lengths in the order they occur in the table. Have students work in pairs.

Materials

- Transparencies 1.2A, 1.2B
- Stick-on notes
- Centimeter grid paper
- Graph paper
- Scissors

Vocabulary

- mode
- range
- median
- spread

Explore

After ordering the data as a class, have students work on Questions A and B. Then go to Question C. The line plot raises the issue of what effect a missing value has on the median. For Question D, if students have trouble, read aloud the description of the hypothetical class.

- *What facts do we know about this class of students?*
- *How can we use these facts to find a set of name lengths?*
- *Is there more than one possible set of name lengths fitting the description? Why? Why not?*

Display the students' line plots.

Summarize

For Questions A and B, create one strip for the original 21 values and the other for the 22 values, and mark the median. Hold up the strip with 21 values.

- *For the 21 values, the fold occurred on a 12. The same number of values are before the fold and after the fold. The median name length is 12 letters.*

Materials

- Student notebooks

continued on next page

Hold up the strip of 22 values.

- *For the strip of 22 values, the fold occurred between 12 and 13. With an even number of values, the median is the number halfway between the two middle values. In this case, the median name length is $12\frac{1}{2}$.*

Direct students to look at the table and graph of the original data.

- *Where is the median name length of 12 letters located on the line plot?*
- *How does the median compare to the mode in this data set?*
- *After adding Suzanne Mannerstrale's name, how does the median compare to the mode?*
- *Can the median have the same value as the mode?*
- *If we had many data values, folding a strip of paper to find the median would be inefficient. Can you think of another way to find the median?*
- *Now look at Question C. What is the median?*

For Question D, the goal is not for students to determine all possible answers, but to realize that many solutions are possible. Have students display their line plots.

- *How are the different line plots alike? Different? Why?*

ACE Assignment Guide for Problem 1.2

Core 2, 5–12
Other *Applications* 3, 4; *Connections* 26–28; unassigned choices from previous problems

Adapted For suggestions about adapting Exercises 3–6 and other ACE exercises, see the CMP *Special Needs Handbook*.

Answers to Problem 1.2

A. 1. The crease occurs on 12.
   2. There are 10 values to the left of the crease.
   3. There are 10 values to the right of the crease.
   4. The median is 12 letters.
B. 1. The crease occurs between 12 and 13.
   2. There are 11 values to the left of the crease.
   3. There are 11 values to the right of the crease.
   4. The median is $12\frac{1}{2}$ letters.
C. The median is 10 letters. The mode is 9.
D. 1. Answers will vary. A correct answer will have a set of 15 names with lengths varying from 8 to 16 letters, with the value 12 occurring most frequently.

2. Possible line plots:

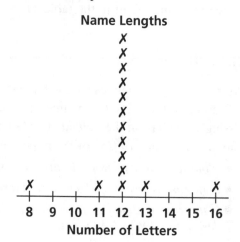

3. Answers will vary. Students may discuss mode and range or the intervals in which the data cluster.

Goals

- Recognize how the median, as a measure of center, responds to changes in the number and magnitude of data values

- Use line plots to display data distributions

In this problem, students explore how responsive the median is to changes in the data values. Does it change if we add a very large or a very small value to the data? How does it react if we make other changes in the data? The idea of the median and its stability is important in making judgments about statistical data.

Launch 1.3

Explain to students that they are going to explore what happens to the median when the data set changes. They will be asked to add and subtract name lengths written on index cards to determine if the median changes. Since they worked on determining the median in Problem 1.2 using grid paper, you might want to talk about how using the index cards to find the median is different.

Ask each group of students to prepare ten index cards as described in the Student Edition. Have students refer to the data in their books, or display Transparency 1.3. Once they have ordered the names from shortest to longest, have them determine the median ($11\frac{1}{2}$ letters).

Suggested Question Work with the class to find an example for Question A.

- *Let's look at Question A, part (1). Starting with the ten cards, we need to see if we can remove two names without changing the median. Which names might we choose?* (You could, for example, remove the shortest name and the longest name.)

When students understand the nature of the questions in the problem, let them work in small groups on Problem 1.3. Ask them to find at least three possibilities for each question. Remind them to keep a record of what they find out.

Use Think-Pair-Share to do the Explore.

Explore 1.3

While students are working on the problem, take time to work with students that are having difficulty. Work through a conjecture they suggest and see how it changes the median.

Summarize 1.3

For each part of the problem, have one or two groups present examples that meet the criteria. You want students to realize that the median is a fairly stable value. It is defined by position; it always marks the midpoint in an ordered set of data. They will later see that this important characteristic makes the median a useful number to statisticians.

Use Question C, part (2), to point out that adding a very large number has little effect on the median. Adding 1,019 to the data has the same effect on the median as adding 16. In Question B, part (2), the median would increase to 12 whether we added 16 and 17 or 900 and 1,000.

1.3 Experimenting With the Median

Mathematical Goals

- Recognize how the median, as a measure of center, responds to changes in the number and magnitude of data values
- Use line plots to display data distributions

Launch

Explain to students that they are going to explore what happens to the median when the data set changes. They will be asked to add and subtract name lengths written on index cards to determine if the median changes. Since they worked on determining the median in Problem 1.2 using grid paper, you might want to talk about how using the index cards to find the median is different.

Ask each group of students to prepare ten index cards as described in the Student Edition. Have students refer to the data in their books, or display Transparency 1.3. Once they have ordered the names from shortest to longest, have them determine the median ($11\frac{1}{2}$ letters). Then, work with the class to find an example for Question A.

- *Let's look at Question A part (1). Starting with the ten cards, we need to see if we can take away two names without changing the median. Which names might we choose?*

When students understand the nature of the questions in the problem, let them work in small groups on Problem 1.3. Ask them to find at least three possibilities for each question. Remind them to keep a record of what they find out. Use Think-Pair-Share to do the Explore.

Materials

- Transparency 1.3
- Index cards (20 per group)

Explore

While students are working on the problem, work with students that are having difficulty. Work through a conjecture they suggest and see how it changes the median.

Summarize

For each part of the problem, have one or two groups present examples that meet the criteria. You want students to realize that the median is a fairly stable value. It is defined by position; it always marks the midpoint in an ordered set of data. They will later see that this important characteristic makes the median a useful number to statisticians.

Use Question C, part (2), to point out that adding a very large number has little effect on the median. Adding 1,019 to the data has the same effect on the median as adding 16. In Question B, part (2), the median would increase to 12 whether we added 16 and 17 or 900 and 1,000.

Materials

- Student notebooks

ACE Assignment Guide
for Problem 1.3

Core 13

Other *Connections* 29, 30; unassigned choices from previous problems

Adapted For suggestions about adapting ACE exercises, see the CMP *Special Needs Handbook*.

Answers to Problem 1.3

A. 1. Possible answers: Remove the least value, 8, and the greatest value, 14; remove the two middle values; the median remains $11\frac{1}{2}$. NOTE: The median marks the midpoint in an ordered set of data; there will always be the same number of data values before and after this midpoint. If students understand this, they can use this fact to help them determine on which side(s) of the median and with what data values they need to make changes.

  2. Possible answers: Remove 8 and 9; remove 10 and 11; the median increases to 12.

  3. Possible answers: Remove both 12's; remove both 14's; the median decreases to 11.

B. 1. Possible answers: Add 11 and 12; add 1 and 2,000; the median remains $11\frac{1}{2}$.

  2. Possible answers: Add 16 and 17; add 900 and 1,000; the median increases to 12.

  3. Possible answers: Add 4 and 5; add the two 11's; the median decreases to 11.

C. 1. The median increases to 12.

  2. The median increases to 12.

Goals

- Identify whether data are categorical or numerical

- Use bar graphs to display data distributions

- Understand how median, mode, and range relate to numerical and categorical data

This problem may provoke some lively discussion about how the questions should be interpreted and how the data might be collected. Let some of this discussion occur. The goal is to have students think about the *kinds of responses*, not actually to gather data.

Mathematics Background

For background on different types of data, see page 4.

You may want to have your class collect its own data and spend some time comparing the students' results with the data provided in the Student Edition. You could also have them make bar graphs to display the data they collect.

Launch 1.4

Refer students to the Getting Ready. You may use Transparency 1.4A. Have a brief discussion about numerical and categorical data.

Suggested Questions Then ask students to:

- *Look over these questions, and think about how you would respond to each. Which questions have words or categories as answers? Which questions have numbers as answers?*

Answers to Getting Ready

It may be helpful to display their answers on posters in two groups:

Questions with Categorical Data Answers

- *In which month were you born?*

- *What is your favorite kind of pet?*

- *Who is your favorite author?*

Questions with Numerical Data Answers

- *How many pets do you have?*

- *How much time do you spend watching television in a day?*

- *What is your highest score in the game?*

- *How many movies have you watched in the last week?*

You might want to keep the poster with these questions displayed as students may decide to use these questions for their final *Is Anyone Typical?* project.

Suggested Question To help students summarize what they know about the distinction between categorical and numerical data, and to launch the next part of the problem (reading information from graphs), ask:

- *What other kinds of questions can you ask about pets that give either categorical or numerical answers?* (Possible categorical answer: What kind of pet do you own? Possible numerical answer: How old is your pet?)

Read the rest of the problem aloud with the students. Look at the pet data (without the graphs), and have students discuss the answers to the questions "What is your favorite kind of pet?" and "How many pets do you have?" in pairs.

Let your students make conjectures about where the data were collected, making sure they justify their responses. After they have discussed their ideas, you may want to reveal that the students who actually provided these data live in rural North Carolina.

We recommend that you launch the problem in two stages. In the first stage, help your students understand why they cannot find the median or range of categorical data. During this stage, students should work with their books closed.

To prepare students to work on answering the questions about the graphs in Problem 1.4, one teacher gave each group a copy of the data listed in a *different order* from the copies she gave to the other groups. This made it likely that students would list the pets in different orders along the horizontal axes of their "favorite pet" graphs. This is how she began the discussion:

- *A class gathered data about their pets. Here are the two questions that each student answered* (write on the board or overhead).

- *What is your favorite kind of pet?*

- *How many pets do you have?*

- *The sheets I just handed you show the data the students collected for each question. For each set of data, I would like you to make a graph and then see if you can find the range, median, and mode. Make your graphs large enough so the whole class will be able to see them.*

When the groups displayed their results, they found that, although they all found the same mode for the favorite pets, each group found a different range and median. This was because they were using the favorite pet data as if it were ordered data. This helped students to understand the fundamental difference between categorical data and numerical data. In the "favorite pet" data, which is categorical data, there is no logical way to order the data, so no median or range can be found (that is, there is no greatest or least data value nor any way to divide the data in half). In the "how many pets" data, the values can be ordered numerically and the data divided in half, and a median and range can be calculated.

Show Transparencies 1.4B and 1.4C. Work with students to make sure they can read the two tables and understand the data as they are presented. Discuss how to read the graphs, highlighting the information shown on the horizontal axis and the vertical axis for each graph. You may want to ask a few questions to sharpen their table and graph comprehension skills. (It is all right for students to move back and forth between the table and the graph. Just make sure they can locate information using both representations.)

Suggested Questions You can ask questions, such as those below, to help students read the data, read between the data, and read beyond the data.

- *How many students chose a dog as their favorite pet?* (7)

- *How many students have 6 pets?* (3)

- *How many total students chose dogs or cats as their favorite pets?* (11)

- *How many people have more than 6 pets?* (7)

- *What do you know about the kinds of pets these students chose as their favorites?* [Answers will vary. The most popular pet (the mode) is the dog, and the second most popular is the cat. The presence of cow, goat, duck, and pig may suggest that some of the students live on farms.]

- *What do you know about how many pets each of the students has?* (Answers will vary. The range is 21. Only 2 people do not have pets. The mode is 2. The data cluster in the interval of 2–6 pets, then spread out with some unusual values occurring in the interval of 14–21 pets.)

- *Do you think our class data would be similar to or different from these students' data?* (Answers may vary.)

Let students work in pairs or small groups to discuss their responses to each of the Problem 1.4 questions.

Explore 1.4

Some students may struggle with Questions C, E, G, or I.

For Question C, students may need to understand that the height of each bar indicates how many students have that number of pets.

Suggested Questions You could ask these questions to help them:

- *How many students have 1 pet?* (2)

- *How many total pets do the bars over 1 pet represent?* (2)

- *How did you figure that out?* (multiplied the number of pets, 1, by the frequency of students who have that number of pets, 2; $1 \times 2 = 2$)

- *How would you find out how many total pets the class has?* (total the product of each number of pets and their corresponding frequency)

For Question E students can find out how many students are in the class using either graph. If they find it using one graph, you may ask them to find it using the other graph.

For those students who need assistance, you could ask:

- *How many students chose cat in the "Favorite Kinds of Pets" graph?* (4)

- *How would knowing how many students chose each pet help you figure out how many students are in the class?* (You could total the number of students who chose each pet to find the total number of students in the class.)

- *How many students have 0 pets in the "Number of Pets" graph?* (2)

- *How would knowing how many students chose each number of pets help you figure out how many students are in the class?* (You could total the number of students who owned each of the number of pets to find the total number of students in the class.)

For Question G, students may need help in understanding that the number of students who chose a favorite pet does not represent the number of students who have that pet.

For Question I, you could ask students who are struggling with locating the median from the graph:

- *How do we find the median?* (order the values and find the midpoint that separates the data into two equal-sized parts)

- *How would you be able to do this using the graph?* (One possible answer: List the number of pets in order as represented on the graph and then find the midpoint.)

Students may need assistance in realizing that 0 number of pets has a frequency of 2, which means 2 students own 0 pets. You can assist them by asking:

- *How many students have 0 number of pets?* (2)

- *How many 0's would you have in your list of values?* (two)

As students work, make sure they record their explanations. Look for strategies to present in the Summary. You may want students to record their work on an overhead transparency to present to the class during the Summary.

Summarize 1.4

Have a class discussion in which teams of students explain their responses to the questions. It is important for students to understand what they can and cannot know from a set of data.

To complete this activity, you may want students to work in pairs for about five minutes to write some questions about these data that can and cannot be answered. For questions that cannot be answered, discuss what information would be needed to answer them.

1.4 Using Different Data Types

PACING 1 day

Mathematical Goals

- Identify whether data are categorical or numerical
- Use bar graphs to display data distributions
- Understand how median, mode, and range relate to numerical and categorical data

Launch

Refer students to the Getting Ready. Use Transparency 1.4A. Have a brief discussion about numerical and categorical data. Consider asking:

- *Which questions have words or categories as answers?*
- *Which questions have numbers as answers?*

To help students summarize the distinction between categorical and numerical data, and to launch the next part of the problem ask:

- *What other kinds of questions can you ask about pets that would give either categorical or numerical answers?*

Read the rest of the problem aloud with the students. Look at the pet data (without the graphs), and have students discuss these questions in pairs: "What is your favorite kind of pet?" and "How many pets do you have?"

Launch the problem in two stages. In the first stage, help your students understand why they cannot find the median or range of categorical data. Have students work with their books closed. Then show Transparencies 1.4B and 1.4C. Work with students to make sure they can read the two tables and understand the data as they are presented. Discuss how to read the graphs. Ask:

- *How many students chose a dog as their favorite pet?*
- *How many students have 6 pets?*
- *How many total students chose dogs or cats as their favorite pets?*
- *What do you know about how many pets each of these students has?*

Let students work in pairs or small groups.

Materials
- Transparencies 1.4A–C

Vocabulary
- categorical data
- numerical data

Explore

Some students may struggle with Questions C, E, G, or I. For Question C, students need to understand that the height of each bar indicates how many students have that number of pets. For Question E help students find out how many students are in the class using either graph. For Question G, students may need help in understanding that the number of students who chose a favorite pet does not represent the number of students who have the pet. For Question I, you could ask students who are struggling with locating the median from the graph:

- *How do we find the median?*
- *How can you do this using the graph?*

Summarize

Have a class discussion in which teams of students explain their responses to the questions. It is important for students to understand what they can and cannot know from a set of data. To complete this activity, you may want students to work in pairs for about five minutes, to write some questions about these data that can and cannot be answered, and to discuss what information may be needed to answer them.

Materials
- Student notebooks

ACE Assignment Guide for Problem 1.4

Core 14–20, 31
Other *Connections* 32, *Extensions* 40–43; unassigned choices from previous problems

Adapted For suggestions about adapting ACE exercises, see the CMP *Special Needs Handbook*.

Answers to Problem 1.4

A. The graph of favorite kinds of pets shows categorical data.

B. The graph of number of pets shows numerical data.

C. 156 pets (multiply each number of pets by its frequency, then add the results)

D. 21 pets (this is the highest number with a bar on top of it on the horizontal axis of the "Number of Pets" graph)

E. 26 students (add the frequency for each favorite kind of pet on the graph or add the frequency for each number of pets on the graph)

F. 4 students

G. This question cannot be answered from the data given.

H. dog

I. $3\frac{1}{2}$ pets

J. The range is 21.

K. This question cannot be answered from the data. Data by individual students were not collected.

L. This question cannot be answered from the data. Data by gender were not collected.

Vertical Bar Graphs and Horizontal Bar Graphs

Goals

- Distinguish between vertical and horizontal bar graphs

- Distinguish how numerical data and categorical data are shown on a horizontal bar graph

- Answer questions using both kinds of bar graphs

This problem is designed to help students understand that bar graphs for either categorical data or numerical data can be displayed horizontally or vertically. Much of students' school experiences involve making and using bar graphs displayed vertically; however, in the popular press, both orientations are used.

Launch 1.5

Display Transparency 1.5A or have students look at the graph of Favorite Kinds of Pets in their books. Another name for this kind of bar graph is *vertical bar graph*.

Suggested Questions

- *Why do you think this kind of bar graph is called a vertical bar graph?*

- *Look at the graph of Favorite Kinds of Pets with the bars going across the page. This kind of bar graph is called a horizontal bar graph. How are the two kinds of bar graphs alike and how are they different?*

- *Look over the questions that are asked. Work with a partner to answer them.*

For vertical bar graph:

- *What information do you find on the horizontal axis?* [The horizontal axis shows the data (kind of pet).]

- *What information do you find on the vertical axis?* (The vertical axis shows the frequencies.)

- *How do you find out how many people chose "dog" as their favorite kind of pet using the vertical bar graph?* (Locate the vertical bar

above "dog." Determine its height by looking at the vertical axis. This is the number of dogs chosen.)

- *What changes would you make in the vertical bar graph to show the new distribution?* (Make the following changes to vertical bar lengths: cat's bar becomes 2 units taller; bird's bar becomes 3 units taller)

- *Compare the vertical bar graph to the horizontal bar graph. How are they alike? How are they different?* [The axes on each graph are swapped; data values are shown using the horizontal axis on a vertical bar graph and on the vertical axis using a horizontal bar graph. The frequency axes are also swapped (i.e., vertical axis on a vertical bar graph and horizontal axis on a horizontal graph).]

NOTE: When you make a horizontal or vertical bar graph of categorical data, order is not important so the data can be arranged in any order along the data axis.

For horizontal bar graph:

- *What information do you find on the horizontal axis?* (The horizontal axis shows the frequencies.)

- *What information do you find on the vertical axis?* [The vertical axis shows the data (kind of pet).]

- *How do you find out how many people chose "dog" as their favorite kind of pet using the horizontal bar graph?* (Locate the horizontal bar extending to the right of "dog." Determine its length by looking at the horizontal axis. This is the number of dogs chosen.)

- *What changes would you make in the horizontal bar graph to show the new distribution?* (Make the following changes to horizontal bar lengths: cat's bar becomes 2 units longer; bird's bar becomes 3 units longer)

We recommend that you complete the launch of the problem by having students look at the vertical bar graph in Problem 1.5. This graph shows numerical data (as opposed to categorical data).

INVESTIGATION 1

Suggested Questions To prepare students to make a horizontal bar graph of the Number of Pets data, help them realize that both axes involve numbers. One axis is numerical data and the other axis shows counts of the frequency.

- *The graph of Number of Pets is a vertical bar graph.*

- *How do you think we can change this to a horizontal bar graph?*

- *On what axis will the data be displayed?* (vertical axis)

- *On what axis will the frequencies be displayed?* (horizontal axis)

- *How can you set up the graph?* (extend bars horizontally from number of pets)

Have students work in pairs to do the problem.

Explore 1.5

The questions are similar to the ones that students have addressed before in other contexts. This problem focuses students' attention on how to determine the answers when using a vertical bar graph and when using a horizontal bar graph. Students may struggle with finding the range. Help them see that it is the range of the number of pets and not of the frequency. If students need assistance to find the median, remind them of any one of the methods used in Problems 1.2–1.4.

Summarize 1.5

Display Transparency 1.5B. Have the class discuss their responses to the questions. Have different students show the strategies they used with each kind of graph. This is another opportunity to have students think about ways to read graphs and about what the median is and how it is determined.

1.5 Vertical Bar Graphs and Horizontal Bar Graphs

Mathematical Goals

- Distinguish between vertical and horizontal bar graphs
- Distinguish how numerical data or categorical data are shown on a horizontal bar graph
- Answer questions using both kinds of bar graphs

Launch

Display Transparency 1.5A or have students look at the graph of Favorite Kinds of Pets in their books.

- *Why do you think this kind of bar graph is called a vertical bar graph?*
- *Look at the graph of Favorite Kinds of Pets with the bars going across the page. This kind of bar graph is called a horizontal bar graph. How are the two kinds of bar graphs alike and how are they different?*
- *Look over the questions that are asked. Work with a partner to answer them.*

To prepare students to make a horizontal bar graph of the Number of Pets data:

- *The graph of Number of Pets is a vertical bar graph.*
- *How do you think we can change this to a horizontal bar graph?*
- *On what axis will the data be displayed?*
- *On what axis will the frequencies be displayed?*
- *How can you set up the graph?*

Have students work in pairs to do the problem.

Materials
- Transparencies 1.5A and 1.5B
- Graph paper

Vocabulary
- vertical bar graph
- horizontal bar graph

Explore

The questions are similar to the ones that students have addressed before in other contexts. This problem focuses students' attention on how to determine the answers when using a vertical bar graph and when using a horizontal bar graph. Students may struggle with finding the range. Help them see that it is the range of the number of pets and not of the frequency. If students need assistance to find the median, remind them of any one of the methods used in Problems 1.2–1.4.

Summarize

Display Transparency 1.5B. Have the class discuss their responses to the questions. Have different students show the strategies they used with each kind of graph. This is another opportunity to have students think about ways to read graphs and about what the median is and how it is determined.

Materials
- Student notebooks

ACE Assignment Guide for Problem 1.5

Core 21

Other *Extensions* 33–39; unassigned choices from previous problems

Adapted For suggestions about adapting ACE exercises, see the CMP *Special Needs Handbook*.

Answers to Problem 1.5

A. The graph at the right shows these data in light gray.

B. 10 students. On the vertical bar graph, locate the data from 6 to 21 pets; add the heights of the bars to determine the total number of students. On the horizontal bar graph, locate the data from 6 to 21 pets; add the lengths of the bars to determine the total number of students.

C. 0 pets. On each graph, locate the least number of pets on the data axis that has bars. This is 0 pets. There are 2 students with no pets.

D. 21 pets. On each graph, locate the data axis and then name the greatest data value.

E. 3.5 pets. For each graph, list the set of data in order from least to greatest. The median is the midpoint between 3 and 4, or 3.5.

F. List the new set of data in order from least to greatest; 3 pets is the median. Adding a 1-unit bar to show one person having 7 pets and adding a 1-unit bar to each of the 1 and 3 number-of-pet bars will change each graph. The graph below shows the additional data in dark gray. Figure 1 reflects the addition.

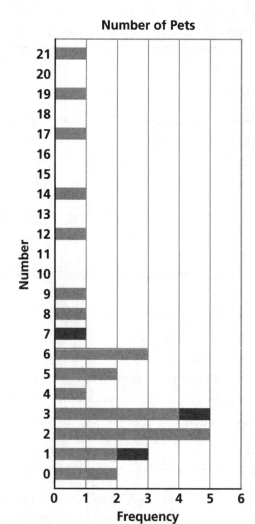

Figure 1

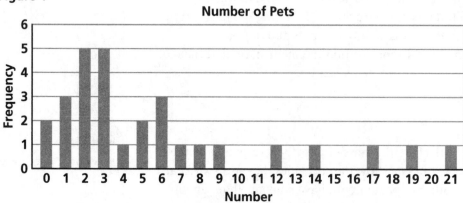

The student edition pages for this investigation begin on the next page.

Notes _____
_____
_____
_____

Looking at Data

The problems in this investigation involve people's names. Family traditions are often involved when a child is named. A person's name may reveal information about his or her ancestors.

Many people have interesting stories about how they were named. Here is one student's story: "I'm a twin, and my mom and dad didn't know they were going to have twins. My sister was born first. She was named Sukey. I was a surprise. My mom named me after the woman in the next hospital bed. Her name was Takara."

- Do you know anything interesting about how you were named or about the history behind your family's name?

6   Data About Us

Notes _____

_____

_____

_____

Did You Know?

Rhoshandiatellyneshiaunneveshenk Koyaanisquatsiuth Williams is the longest name on a birth certificate.

Shortly after Rhoshandiatellyneshiaunneveshenk was born, her father lengthened her first name to 1,019 letters and her middle name to 36 letters. What is a good nickname for her?

1.1 Organizing and Interpreting Data

Most parents do not worry about the number of letters in their children's names. Sometimes though, name length does matter. For example, only a limited number of letters may fit on a bracelet or a library card.

Getting Ready for Problem 1.1

What do you think is the typical number of letters in the full names (first and last names) of your classmates?

• What data do you need to collect and how would you collect it?

• How would you organize and represent your data?

• If a new student joined your class today, how might you use your results to predict the length of that student's name?

Investigation 1 Looking at Data   **7**

Notes _____

_____

_____

_____

The students in Ms. Jee's class made a **line plot** to display the distribution of their class's data.

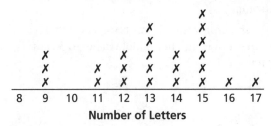

Name Lengths of Ms. Jee's Students

Number of Letters

Another group displayed the same data using a **bar graph.**

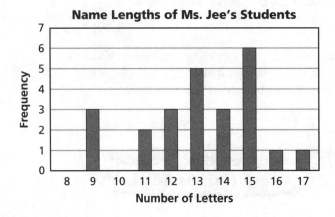

To describe how the data are distributed, you might look at where the data values cluster, how much they vary, and the high and low values.

Problem 1.1 Organizing and Interpreting Data

Examine the line plot and the bar graph.

A. Describe the distribution of the data. Do you see any patterns?

B. How are the two graphs alike? How are they different?

C. How can you use each graph to determine the total number of letters in all the names?

D. Fahimeh Ghomizadeh said, "My name has the most letters, but the bar that shows my name length is one of the shortest on the graph. Why?" How would you answer this question?

8   Data About Us

Notes _____

_____

_____

_____

E. Collect the data for your class's name lengths. Represent the data distribution using a line plot or a bar graph.

F. What are some similarities and differences between the data distribution from Ms. Jee's class and the data distribution from your class?

ACE Homework starts on page 21.

In Africa, a child's name is often very meaningful. Names such as Sekelaga, which means "rejoice," and Tusajigwe, which means "we are blessed," reflect the happiness the family felt at the child's birth. Names such as Mvula, meaning "rain," reflect events that happened at the time the child was born.

 For: Information about African names
Web Code: ame-9031

1.2 Useful Statistics

In the data for Ms. Jee's class, the name length of 15 letters occurs most often. Notice that 15 has the highest stack of X's in the line plot and the tallest bar in the bar graph. We call the most frequent value the **mode** of the data set.

The least value and the greatest value are important values in a data set. They give a sense of the variability in the data. In Ms. Jee's class, the data vary from 9 letters to 17 letters. The difference between the least value and the greatest value is called the **range** of the data. The range of Ms. Jee's class data is 17 − 9, or 8 letters.

Still another important statistic is the **median,** or the midpoint, of the data set.

Notes _____

_____

_____

_____

The table and line plot below show the distribution of the name-length data for Mr. Gray's class. Notice that these data have two modes, 11 letters and 12 letters. We say the distribution is *bimodal*. The data vary from 7 letters to 19 letters. The range of the data is 19 – 7, or 12 letters.

Name Lengths of Mr. Gray's Students	
Name	Number of Letters
Jeffrey Piersonjones	19
Thomas Petes	11
Clarence Jenkins	15
Michelle Hughes	14
Shoshana White	13
Deborah Black	12
Terry Van Bourgondien	19
Maxi Swanson	11
Tonya Stewart	12
Jorge Bastante	13
Richard Mudd	11
Joachim Caruso	13
Robert Northcott	15
Tony Tung	8
Joshua Klein	11
Jan Wong	7
Bob King	7
Veronica Rodriguez	17
Charlene Greene	14
Peter Juliano	12
Linora Haynes	12

Name Lengths of Mr. Gray's Students

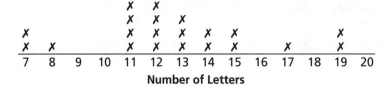

Number of Letters

10   Data About Us

Notes _____

_____

_____

_____

Problem 1.2 Useful Statistics

Here is a way to help you think about how to identify the median. Cut a strip of 21 squares from a sheet of grid paper. Each square is for the length of a student's name in Mr. Gray's class. Write the name lengths of Mr. Gray's students in order from least to greatest on the grid paper as shown.

7	7	8	11	11	11	11	12	12	12	12	13	13	13	14	14	15	15	17	19	19

A. Fold the strip in half.

    1. On what number is the crease caused by the fold?

    2. How many numbers occur to the left of this number?

    3. How many numbers occur to the right of this number?

    4. The median is the number that is the midpoint of a set of data. The same number of data values occurs before and after the median. What is the median for these data?

B. Suppose a new student, Suzanne Mannerstrale, joins Mr. Gray's class. The class now has 22 students. On a strip of 22 squares, list the name lengths, including Suzanne's, in order from least to greatest. Fold the strip in half.

    1. On what number is the crease caused by the fold?

    2. How many numbers occur to the left of the crease?

    3. How many numbers occur to the right of the crease?

    4. What is the median for these data?

C. Suzanne has six pets. She made the line plot shown of her pets' name lengths. Find the median length of her pets' names. Find the mode for the data set.

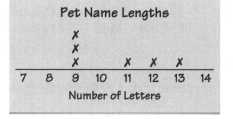

D. There are 15 students in a class. Use the information about the class's name lengths below.

    ● Mode: 12 letters

    ● Median: 12 letters

    ● The data vary from 8 letters to 16 letters

    1. Find a possible set of name lengths for the class.

    2. Make a line plot to display your data distribution.

    3. Compare your graph with the graphs of your classmates. How are the graphs alike? How are they different?

ACE Homework starts on page 21.

Investigation 1 Looking at Data   **11**

Notes _____

_____

_____

_____

You can use the median and the mode of a set of data to describe what is typical about the distribution. They are sometimes called *measures of center*.

Use the following ten names. Write each name on an index card. On the back of each card, write the number of letters in the name. A sample index card is shown below.

Student Name Lengths

Name	Number of Letters
Thomas Petes	11
Michelle Hughes	14
Shoshana White	13
Deborah Black	12
Tonya Stewart	12
Richard Mudd	11
Tony Tung	8
Janice Wong	10
Bobby King	9
Charlene Greene	14

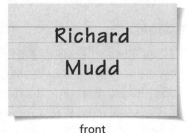

front

back

Order the cards from shortest name length to longest name length, and identify the median of the data.

Problem 1.3 **Experimenting With the Median**

Use your cards to complete each task below. Keep a record of your work.

A. Remove two names from the original data set so that

  1. the median stays the same.

  2. the median increases.

  3. the median decreases.

Notes _____

_____

_____

_____

B. Add two new names to the original data set so that

    1. the median stays the same.

    2. the median increases.

    3. the median decreases.

C. How does the median of the original data set change if you add a name

    1. with 16 letters?

    2. with 1,019 letters?

ACE **Homework starts on page 21.**

Did You Know?

Names from many parts of the world have special origins. European family names (last names) often came from the father's first name. For example, Ian Robertson was the son of Robert, Janos Ivanovich was the son (vich) of Ivan, and John Peters was the son of Peter.

Family names also came from words that described a person's hometown or job. This resulted in such names as William Hill and Gilbert Baker.

Family names in China and Vietnam are almost always one-syllable words that are related to names of ruling families. Chang is one such example.

You can read more about names in books such as *Names from Africa* by Ogonna Chuks-Orji and *Do People Grow on Family Trees?* by Ira Wolfman.

Go Online
PHSchool.com **For:** Information about names
Web Code: ame-9031

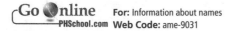

Investigation 1 Looking at Data **13**

Notes _____

_____

_____

_____

1.4 Using Different Data Types

When you are interested in learning more about something, you ask questions about it. Some questions have answers that are words or categories. For example, what is your favorite sport? Other questions have answers that are numbers. For example, how many inches tall are you?

Categorical data are data that are specific labels or names for categories. They are usually not numbers. Suppose you ask people in which month they were born or what kinds of pets they have. Their answers would be categorical data.

Numerical data are data that are counts or measures. Suppose you ask people how tall they are or how many pets they have. Their responses would be numerical data.

Getting Ready for Problem

Read each of the questions below. Which questions have words or categories as answers? Which questions have numbers as answers?

- In which month were you born?
- What is your favorite kind of pet?
- How many pets do you have?
- Who is your favorite author?
- How much time do you spend watching television in a day?
- What's your highest score in the game?
- How many movies have you watched in the past week?

Notes _____

_____

_____

_____

The kinds of pets people have often depend on where they live. People who live in cities often have small pets. People who live on farms often have large pets. People who live in apartments sometimes cannot have pets at all.

One middle-school class gathered data about their pets by tallying students' responses to these questions:

- What is your favorite kind of pet?
- How many pets do you have?

Notes _____

_____

_____

_____

`

The students made tables to show the tallies or frequencies. Then they made bar graphs to display the data distributions.

Do you think the students surveyed live in a city, the suburbs, or the country? Explain.

Number of Pets

Number	Frequency
0	2
1	2
2	5
3	4
4	1
5	2
6	3
7	0
8	1
9	1
10	0
11	0
12	1
13	0
14	1
15	0
16	0
17	1
18	0
19	1
20	0
21	1

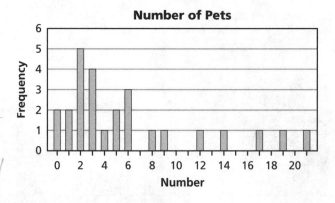

16 Data About Us

Notes

Favorite Kinds of Pets

Pet	Frequency
cat	4
dog	7
fish	2
bird	2
horse	3
goat	1
cow	2
rabbit	3
duck	1
pig	1

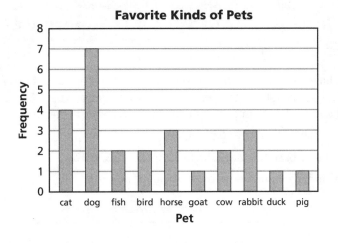

Favorite Kinds of Pets

Problem 1.4 Using Different Data Types

Decide whether each question can be answered by using data from the graphs and tables the students created. If so, give the answer and explain how you got it. If not, explain why not and tell what additional information you would need to answer the question.

A. Which graph shows categorical data?

B. Which graph shows numerical data?

C. What is the total number of pets the students have?

D. What is the greatest number of pets a student has?

E. How many students are in the class?

F. How many students chose cats as their favorite kind of pet?

G. How many cats do students have as pets?

H. What is the mode for the favorite kind of pet?

I. What is the median number of pets students have?

J. What is the range of the numbers of pets students have?

K. Tomas is a student in this class. How many pets does he have?

L. Do the girls have more pets than the boys?

ACE Homework starts on page 21.

Investigation 1 Looking at Data **17**

Notes _____

_____

_____

_____

1.5 Vertical Bar Graphs and Horizontal Bar Graphs

You have used bar graphs to display distributions of data. *Vertical bar graphs* display data on the horizontal axis with vertical bars. On vertical bar graphs, the heights can be compared to the vertical frequency axis.

Look at the vertical bar graph below.

- What information does the horizontal axis show?
- What information does the vertical axis show?

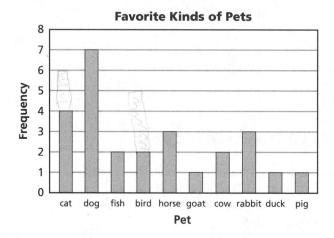

- How do you find out how many people chose "dog" as their favorite kind of pet using the vertical bar graph?

Suppose five more students are surveyed. Three identify birds as their favorite kind of pet. Two identify cats as their favorite kind of pet.

- What changes would you make in the vertical bar graph to show the new distribution?

18 Data About Us

Notes _____

_____

_____

_____

Below is the distribution of the original pet data shown on a *horizontal bar graph*.

- Compare the vertical bar graph to the horizontal bar graph. How are they alike? How are they different?

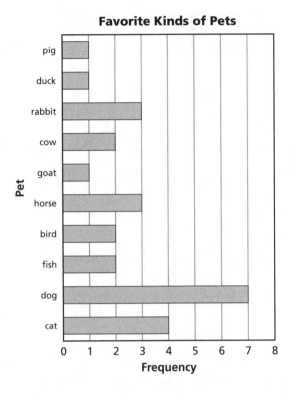

Favorite Kinds of Pets

- How do you find out how many people chose "dog" as their favorite kind of pet using the horizontal bar graph?

Suppose five more students were surveyed. Three identify birds as their favorite kind of pet. Two identify cats as their favorite kind of pet.

- What changes would you make in the horizontal bar graph to show the new distribution?

Notes _____

_____

_____

_____

Problem 1.5 Vertical Bar Graphs and Horizontal Bar Graphs

Below is a vertical bar graph showing the distribution of the number of pets students have.

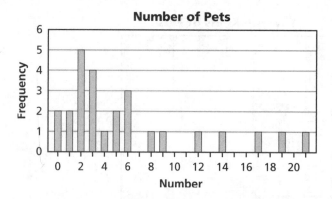

Number of Pets

A. Make a horizontal bar graph to show this distribution of data.

For each question below, explain:

- how you can find the answer to the question using the vertical bar graph

- how you can find the answer to the question using the horizontal bar graph

B. How many students in the class have more than five pets?

C. What is the least number of pets that any student in the class has?

D. What is the greatest number of pets that any student in the class has?

E. What is the median number of pets?

F. Three students were absent when these data were collected. Malcolm has 7 pets, Makana has 1 pet, and Jake has 3 pets. Add their data to each graph. What is the median number of pets now?

ACE Homework starts on page 21.

20 Data About Us

Notes

Applications

For Exercises 1 and 2, use the names of Mr. Young's students listed below.

Ben Foster	Rosita Ramirez
Ava Baker	Kimberly Pace
Lucas Fuentes	Paula Wheeler
Juan Norinda	Darnell Fay
Ron Weaver	Jeremy Yosho
Bryan Wong	Cora Harris
Toby Vanhook	Corey Brooks
Katrina Roberson	Tijuana Degraffenreid

1. Make a table showing the length of each name. Then make both a line plot and a bar graph of the name lengths.

2. What is the typical name length for Mr. Young's students? Use the mode, median, and range to help you answer this question.

For Exercises 3–6, make a line plot or bar graph of a data distribution that fits each description.

3. 24 names, with a range of 12 letters

4. 7 names, with a median length of 14 letters

5. 13 names, with a median length of 13 letters, and with data that vary from 8 letters to 17 letters

6. 16 names, with a median length of $14\frac{1}{2}$ letters, and with data that vary from 11 letters to 20 letters

Notes _____

_____

_____

_____

For Exercises 7–12, use the bar graph below.

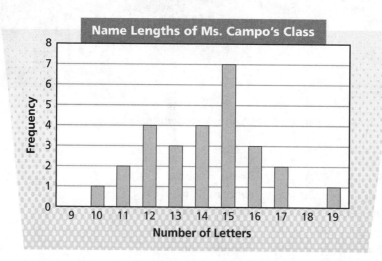

7. How does the data distribution from Ms. Campo's class compare with the data distribution from Mr. Young's class in Exercise 1?

8. **Multiple Choice** For Ms. Campo's students, which value (name length) occurs most frequently?

   A. 12 letters **B.** 14 letters **C.** 15 letters **D.** 16 letters

9. **Multiple Choice** What is the name of the value found in Exercise 8?

   F. range **G.** median **H.** mode **J.** none of these

10. How many students are in Ms. Campo's class? Explain how you got your answer.

11. What is the range of name lengths for this class?

12. What is the median name length? Explain how you got your answer.

13. Look at the table and graph for Number of Pets from the introduction to Problem 1.4. Four new students join the class. One student has 3 pets, two students each have 7 pets, and the last student has 16 pets.

    a. Copy the graph and show these data included.

    b. With these new data included, does the median change or stay the same? Explain your reasoning.

Go Online
PHSchool.com

For: Multiple-Choice Skills Practice
Web Code: ama-8154

Notes _____

_____

_____

_____

For Exercises 14–20, tell whether the answers to the questions are numerical or categorical data.

14. What is your height in centimeters?

15. What is your favorite musical group?

16. What would you like to do after you graduate from high school?

17. Are students in Mr. Perez's class older than students in Ms. Sato's class?

18. What kind(s) of transportation do you use to get to school?

19. How much time do you spend doing homework?

20. On a scale of 1 to 7, with 7 being outstanding and 1 being poor, how would you rate the cafeteria food?

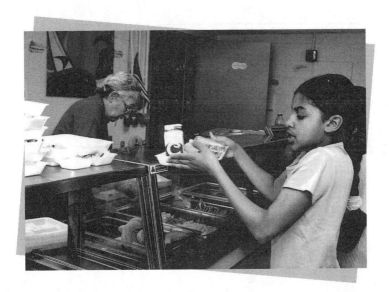

21. Use the graph for Name Lengths from Exercises 7–12. Make a horizontal bar graph of Ms. Campo's students' name length data.

  a. What is the median name length? How does it compare with the answer you found in Exercise 12? Why do you think this is so?

  b. A new student joins Ms. Campo's class. The student has a name length of 16 letters. Add this data value to your graph. Does the median change? Explain.

Investigation 1 Looking at Data   **23**

Notes

Connections

For Exercises 22–25, use the bar graphs below. The graphs show information about a class of middle-school students.

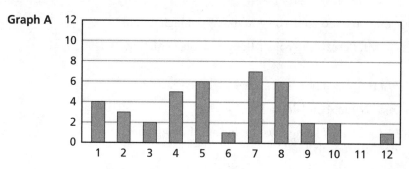

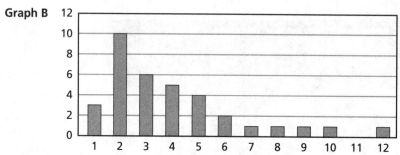

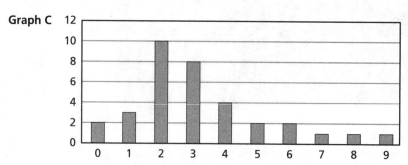

22. Which graph might show the number of children in the students' families? Explain.

23. Which graph might show the birth months of the students? Explain. **Hint:** Months are often written using numbers instead of names. For example, 1 means January, 2 means February, etc.

24. Which graph might show the number of toppings students like on their pizzas? Explain.

25. Give a possible title, a label for the vertical axis, and a label for the horizontal axis for each graph based on your answers to Exercises 22–24.

Notes

_____

_____

_____

_____

For Exercises 26–31, use the graph below. The graph shows the number of juice drinks 100 middle-school students consume in one day.

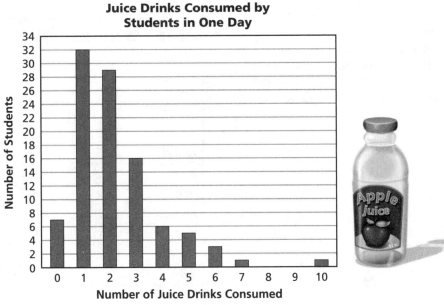

Juice Drinks Consumed by Students in One Day

26. A student used this graph to estimate that the median number of juice drinks students consume in a day is five. How can you tell that this estimate is not correct without finding the median?

27. Another student estimates that the median number of juice drinks is 1. Explain why the student is not correct.

28. **Multiple Choice** What is the range of these data?

   A. 9 drinks   **B.** 10 drinks   **C.** 11 drinks   **D.** 12 drinks

29. **a.** What fraction of the students consumed two juice drinks?

   b. What percent of the students consumed three juice drinks?

30. What is the total number of juice drinks these 100 students consume in one day? How did you determine your answer?

31. Are these data numerical or categorical? Explain.

32. Alex has a rat that is three years old. He wonders if his rat is old compared to other rats. At the pet store, he finds out that the median age for a rat is $2\frac{1}{2}$ years.

   a. What does the median tell Alex about the life span for a rat?

   b. How would knowing how the data vary from the least value to the greatest value help Alex predict the life span of his rat?

Homework Help Online
PHSchool.com
For: Help with Exercise 29
Web Code: ame-8129

Investigation 1 Looking at Data   **25**

Notes _____

_____

_____

_____

Extensions

For Exercises 33–39, use the bar graphs below.

A greeting card store sells stickers and street signs with first names on them. The store ordered 12 stickers and 12 street signs for each name. The table and the four bar graphs show the numbers of stickers and street signs that remain for the names that begin with the letter A.

Sales of Stickers and Street Signs

Name	Stickers Remaining	Street Signs Remaining
Aaron	1	9
Adam	2	7
Alicia	7	4
Allison	2	3
Amanda	0	11
Amber	2	3
Amy	3	3
Andrea	2	4
Andrew	8	6
Andy	3	5
Angela	8	4
Ana	10	7

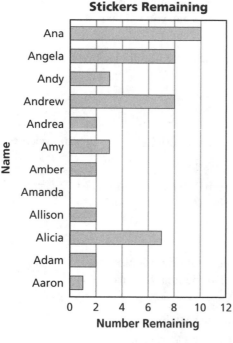

**Graph A:
Stickers Remaining**

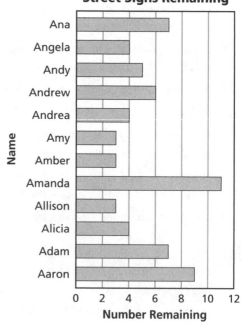

**Graph B:
Street Signs Remaining**

STUDENT PAGE

Notes

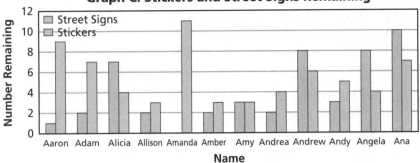

Graph C: Stickers and Street Signs Remaining

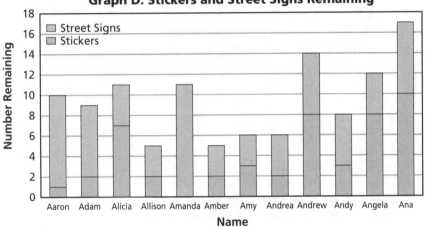

Graph D: Stickers and Street Signs Remaining

33. Use Graph A. How many Alicia stickers are left? How many Alicia stickers have been sold? Explain.

34. Use Graph B. How many Alicia street signs are left? How many Alicia street signs have been sold? Explain.

35. Are the stickers more popular than the street signs? Explain.

36. If each sticker costs $1.50, how much money has the store collected from selling name stickers for names beginning with the letter A?

37. For which name has the store sold the most stickers? For which name has the store sold the least stickers?

38. Graph C is a *double bar graph*. Use this graph to determine the name(s) for which the number of street signs sold and the number of stickers sold are the same.

39. Graph D is a *stacked bar graph*. Use this graph to determine whether some names are more popular than others. Justify your answer.

Notes _____

_____

_____

_____

These data show the kinds of pets middle-school students have. From these data we cannot tell how many students were surveyed. We only know that 841 pets were counted.

**Kinds of Pets
Students Have**

Pet	Frequency
bird	61
cat	184
dog	180
fish	303
gerbil	17
guinea pig	12
hamster	32
horse	28
rabbit	2
snake	9
turtle	13
Total	**841**

40. Make a bar graph to display the distribution of these data. Think about how you will design and label the horizontal and vertical axes.

41. Use the information displayed in your graph to write a paragraph about the pets these students have. Compare these data with the data in Problem 1.4.

42. Jane said that close to 50% of the animals owned were birds, cats, or dogs. Do you agree or disagree? Explain.

43. What might be a good estimate of how many students were surveyed? (Use the data about number of pets each student had from Problem 1.4 to help you.) Explain.

Notes _____

_____

_____

_____

Mathematical Reflections 1

In this investigation, you learned some ways to describe what is typical about a set of data. The following questions will help you summarize what you have learned.

Think about your answers to these questions. Discuss your ideas with other students and your teacher. Then write a summary of your findings in your notebook.

1. How are a table of data, a line plot, and a bar graph alike? How are they different?

2. What does the mode tell you about the distribution of a set of data? Can the mode be used to describe both categorical data and numerical data?

3. What does the median tell you about the distribution of a set of data? Can the median be used to describe both categorical data and numerical data?

4. Can the mode and the median of a set of data be the same values? Can they be different? Explain.

5. Why is it helpful to give the range when you describe the distribution of a set of data? Can the range be used to describe both categorical and numerical data?

6. How are the least and greatest values of a set of data related to the range of that data?

7. How can you describe what is typical about the distribution of a set of data?

Unit Project   What's Next?

To carry out a research project about characteristics of the typical middle-school student, you will need to pose questions. What questions might you ask that would have categorical data as answers? What questions might you ask that have numerical data as answers? How would you display the information you gather about each of these questions? Write your thoughts in your notebook.

Investigation 1 Looking at Data   **29**

Notes _____

_____

_____

_____

Investigation

ACE
Assignment Choices

Differentiated Instruction
Solutions for All Learners

Problem 1.1
Core 1, 22–25

Problem 1.2
Core 2, 5–12
Other *Applications* 3, 4; *Connections* 26–28;
unassigned choices from previous problems

Problem 1.3
Core 13
Other *Connections* 29, 30; unassigned choices from
previous problems

Problem 1.4
Core 14–20, 31
Other *Connections* 32, *Extensions* 40–43;
unassigned choices from previous problems

Problem 1.5
Core 21
Other *Extensions* 33–39; unassigned choices from
previous problems

Adapted For suggestions about adapting
Exercises 3–6 and other ACE exercises, see
the CMP *Special Needs Handbook*.

Applications

1.

Name Lengths

Name	Number of Letters
Ben Foster	9
Ava Baker	8
Lucas Fuentes	12
Juan Norinda	11
Ron Weaver	9
Bryan Wong	9
Toby Vanhook	11
Katrina Roberson	15
Rosita Ramirez	13
Kimberly Pace	12
Paula Wheeler	12
Darnell Fay	10
Jeremy Yosho	11
Cora Harris	10
Corey Brooks	11
Tijuana Degraffenreid	20

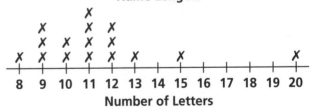

Name Lengths

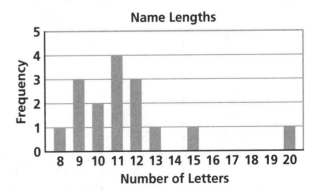

Name Lengths

2. The median name length is 11 letters, and the range of the data is 12 letters. A name length of 20 letters is somewhat unusual. The typical number of letters is clustered around the median in an interval of 8–13 letters or 9–12 letters. The mode is the same as the median in this example, although 9 letters and 12 letters occur almost as frequently as the mode.

3. Possible answer:

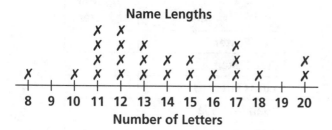

Name Lengths

Number of Letters

4. Possible answer:

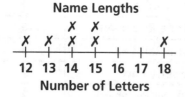

Name Lengths

Number of Letters

5. Possible answer:

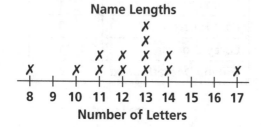

Name Lengths

Number of Letters

6. Possible answer:

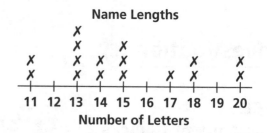

Name Lengths

Number of Letters

7. Possible answer: The data distribution from Ms. Campo's class shows that the typical number of letters is clustered around the median in an interval of 10–17 or 12–16 letters. This is slightly higher than the data distribution from Mr. Young's class. The data for Ms. Campo's class vary from 10 to 19 letters; the data for Mr. Young's class vary from 8 to 20 letters.

8. C　　　　　　　　**9.** H

10. 27 students; the bar for each number represents the number of students with that name length, so adding the bar heights $(1 + 2 + 4 + 3 + 4 + 7 + 3 + 2 + 1)$ gives the total number of students.

11. 9 letters

12. 14 letters; there are 27 name lengths, so the median occurs at the fourteenth name length, which is 14 letters.

13. a. (Figure 2)

　　b. The median will change because three pieces of the new data are above the original median and only one is below.

14. numerical　　　　**15.** categorical

16. categorical

17. categorical (NOTE: The question asks for "yes" or "no," not for a number.)

18. categorical

Figure 2

Number of Pets

42　Data About Us

19. numerical   **20.** numerical

21.

Name Lengths of Ms. Campo's Class

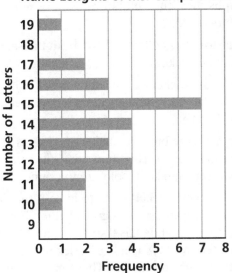

a. The median name length is 14 letters. It is the same data, just represented horizontally, so the median remains the same. (There are 27 data values; the median is the fourteenth data value, which happens to be 14 letters, in an ordered list of the data.)

b.

Name Lengths of Ms. Campo's Class

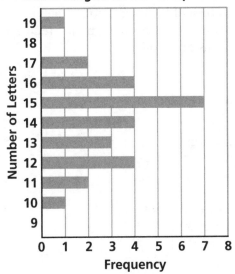

The median name length is $14\frac{1}{2}$ letters (There are now 28 data values; the median is the average of the fourteenth and fifteenth data values, which are 14 and 15 letters, in an ordered list of the data values.)

Connections

22. Possible answer: Graphs A and B; Graph C has values that are 0; since the students are children, their families could not have 0 children. Some students might argue that Graph A is not correct because it is unlikely that there will be a lot of families with 5, 7, and 8 children.

23. Possible answer: Graphs A and B; Graph A and Graph B are labeled 1 through 12 on the horizontal axis. However, some students might argue that in Graph B, it is unlikely that 10 students were born in February. Graph C only has labels from 0 to 9 on the horizontal axis.

24. Any of the graphs could show numbers of pizza toppings. Some students might argue that Graph C is correct because most of their friends like two or three toppings.

25. Possible answers:

Graph A: Birth Months of Students, Birth Month, Frequency

Graph B: Number of Children in Students' Families, Number of Children, Frequency

Graph C: Number of Pizza Toppings, Number of Toppings, Frequency

26. The median is the number that separates the ordered data in half. The number of people that consume 5 juice drinks in one day is near the upper end of the data, so 5 cannot be the median.

27. There are 100 students, so the median is between the fiftieth and fifty-first ordered data values. A total of 39 students consumed 0 or 1 juice drink in one day. This means the median is greater than 1 juice drink, because the fiftieth value will be in the bar that represents 2 juice drinks in one day.

28. B

29. a. $\frac{29}{100}$ **b.** $\frac{16}{100} = 16\%$

30. The total number of juice drinks students consumed is determined by evaluating each bar of the graph:

7 people $\times$ 0 juice drinks = 0 juice drinks

32 people $\times$ 1 juice drink = 32 juice drinks

29 people $\times$ 2 juice drinks = 58 juice drinks

16 people $\times$ 3 juice drinks = 48 juice drinks

6 people × 4 juice drinks = 24 juice drinks

5 people × 5 juice drinks = 25 juice drinks

3 people × 6 juice drinks = 18 juice drinks

1 person × 7 juice drinks = 7 juice drinks

1 person × 10 juice drinks = 10 juice drinks

So, 100 students consumed a total of 222 juice drinks in one day.

31. Numerical; the answer to the question, "How many juice drinks do you consume in one day?", is a number.

32. a. Half of all rats live less than $2\frac{1}{2}$ years, and half live longer than $2\frac{1}{2}$ years.

b. If Alex knew the greatest age of a rat, he would know how much longer his rat could possibly live.

Extensions

33. The bar height, 7, represents the number of stickers left. Because there were 12 to begin with, 5 have been sold.

34. The bar height, 4, represents the number of street signs left. Because there were 12 signs to begin with, 8 have been sold.

35. The bar graphs show that the number of stickers remaining is less than the number of street signs remaining. Students may want to debate this because of the "peaks" in the data. You will want to remind them that the bar graphs show the number remaining, not the number sold.

36. The store has collected $144 from the sale of 96 name stickers.

37. The most stickers, 12, have been sold for Amanda. The fewest stickers, 2, have been sold for Ana.

38. For Amy, the bars for stickers and signs are the same height. This shows that the numbers of stickers and signs sold are the same.

39. The stacked bars allow us to look at the data for stickers and street signs together. For example, Amanda has 0 stickers and 11 street signs left, while Alicia has 7 stickers and 4 street signs remaining. These names have the same total number of items remaining because the stacked bars are the same height. Allison and Amber are the most popular names because their stacked bars are the shortest. Ana is the least popular name because it has the highest stacked bar.

40. Possible answer: (Figure 3)

The challenge for students will be developing the scale for the vertical axis. Because of the range of the data (2 to 303 pets), the scale probably needs to be numbered by at least tens or twenties.

Figure 3

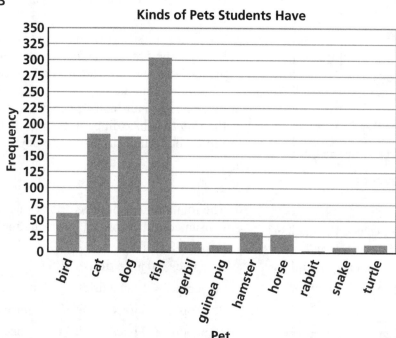

Kinds of Pets Students Have

41. Possible answer: Fish occur the most frequently, followed by cats and dogs. In Problem 1.4, dogs occur most frequently, followed by cats, but the numbers are much smaller. The remaining pets are not like those of the students in Problem 1.4. Many of these pets are "indoor" pets. In Problem 1.4, many of the pets were "outdoor" pets that would live on a farm or in more rural areas.

42. Agree, because $\frac{61 + 184 + 180}{841} = \frac{425}{841} \approx 50\%$.

43. Answers will vary. Some students may immediately respond that 841 people were surveyed, indicating that each person surveyed had one pet. Other students may note that this response does not take into account that it is likely that some people surveyed had no pets or had more than one pet. This may lead students to look back at the data from Problem 1.4, where they know both the total numbers of pets and the number of people surveyed. From these data, students might find the median number of pets per person to be $3\frac{1}{2}$. Then they might divide 841 pets by 3.5 per student to get the possible number surveyed (about 240 students). Some students may raise a concern that the data from Problem 1.4 may reflect a special group of students who live in the country, and therefore, often have more pets; perhaps these particular data do not reflect the kinds of people surveyed for Problem 1.4. Students may have other strategies as well.

Possible Answers to Mathematical Reflections

1. A table of data, a line plot, and a bar graph are all tools for organizing and visualizing data. All three indicate the possible values of the item being measured (for example, 10 letters, 11 letters). A line plot and a bar graph indicate the number of times each value occurs.

   A line plot has a horizontal axis that shows the possible values with marks above the numbers indicating the number of times each value occurs.

Like the line plot, a bar graph has a horizontal axis showing the possible values. Instead of using marks, the number of times a value occurs is indicated by the height of a bar over the value. A vertical axis indicates the frequency, corresponding to the height of each bar.

A line plot is usually vertical, but a bar graph can be vertical or horizontal.

2. The mode is the value in a data set that occurs most frequently. There may be more than one mode, and a mode may occur at any location in the data. The mode can describe both categorical and numerical data. In categorical data, the mode would tell you which category occurs most frequently, and in numerical data the mode tells you which numerical value occurs most frequently.

3. The median is the value that divides an ordered set of data in half; half the data are below the median, and half the data are above the median. The median is not easily affected by the addition of very high or very low values. A median can only be used with numerical data because categorical data cannot be ordered.

4. The mode and the median for a set of data may or may not be the same. For the data set 1, 2, 3, 3, 4, 5, 6, both the median and the mode are 3. For the data set 1, 1, 1, 3, 5, 6, 6, the mode is 1 and the median is 3.

5. The range indicates how spread out the data are. Combined with a measure of center such as the median or the mode, the range helps to give a picture of the data. For example, if you know a data set has a median of 20, you know where the middle of the data set is. If, in addition, you know the range is 4 (or 60), you have a much better idea of what the data may look like. Range can only be used to describe numerical data.

6. The range is the difference between the least and greatest data values.

7. The mode, median, and range can be used to describe what is typical about a data set. You can also give an interval in which most of the data values fall. Giving information about the shape of the data (peaks, gaps, clusters) also helps describe what is typical.

Investigation 2 — Using Graphs to Explore Data

Mathematical and Problem-Solving Goals

- Group numerical data in equal intervals and display their distribution using a stem-and-leaf plot

- Find measures of center and variation, including range and how data vary from the least to the greatest values, when a distribution is displayed using a stem-and-leaf plot

- Compare two distributions displayed using back-to-back stem-and-leaf plots

- Compare two distributions using statistics, such as median, range, and how the data vary from least to greatest values

- Identify outliers in a distribution

- Display distributions of paired-data values on coordinate graphs

- Explore relationships between paired-data values whose distributions are displayed using coordinate graphs

- Explore intervals for scaling the vertical axis (y-axis) and the horizontal axis (x-axis)

Summary of Problems

Problem 2.1 Traveling to School

Students use stem-and-leaf plots to group middle school students' travel times, which are more variable than data in earlier sets.

Problem 2.2 Jumping Rope

Students use back-to-back stem-and-leaf plots to compare jump-rope endurance for two classes.

Problem 2.3 Relating Height to Arm Span

Students make a coordinate graph to explore whether there is a relationship between height and arm span.

Problem 2.4 Relating Travel Time to Distance

Students use a coordinate graph of the data from Problem 2.1 to determine whether there is a relationship between the times the students spend traveling to school and the distances between their homes and school.

Mathematics Background

For background on data reduction and covariation, see pages 6–8.

	Suggested Pacing	Materials for Students	Materials for Teachers	ACE Assignments
All	5 days	Calculators, blank transparencies and transparency markers (optional), student notebooks, graph paper	Blank transparencies and transparency markers (optional), large grid paper (optional), colored stick-on dots (optional)	
2.1	1 day		Transparencies 2.1A–C, local street map (optional)	1–4
2.2	1 day		Transparency 2.2	5–7, 10, 13, 14
2.3	$1\frac{1}{2}$ days	Yardsticks (or meter sticks or tape measures), string (optional)	Transparencies 2.3A and 2.3B; large grid paper (optional)	8, 11
2.4	1 day	Labsheets 2.4, 2ACE Exercise 15	Transparency 2.4	9, 12, 15
MR	$\frac{1}{2}$ day			

Traveling to School

Goals

- Group numerical data in equal intervals and display their distribution using a stem-and-leaf plot

- Find measures of center and variation, including range and how data vary from the least to the greatest values, when a distribution is displayed using a stem-and-leaf plot

   Students explore two different contexts (Problems 2.1 and 2.2) in which the data collected are more variable than those in earlier data sets.

   Representations such as line plots and bar graphs are not suitable for displaying these data; the patterns within the data sets can only be seen when the data are grouped. The stem-and-leaf plot provides a representational tool that permits grouping data in equal intervals.

   This lesson begins to expand the students' ability to look for patterns in data, rather than look at individual data items. A data list or a data table rarely shows where data tend to cluster, nor the gaps between data that can also be important to understanding the complete set.

Launch 2.1

Display Transparencies 2.1A and 2.1B. To engage students in the context of the problem and the data set, refer them to the table of data and the first two questions in the Getting Ready.

Suggested Questions Ask the following and have them work on it for a few minutes before you have a whole class discussion:

- *Look at the table of data. What are the three questions that the students asked to collect this data?* (How long does it take for you to travel to school? How far do you travel to get to school? How do you get to school?)

- *Describe how you think they collected the data to answer each of these questions.* (Possible answer: questionnaire)

Make sure you review with students how the data for distance are in decimal form in multiples of a quarter mile, or 0.25. Students will become more comfortable with the data once they review its format.

Refer students to the third question in the Getting Ready.

- *Would a line plot be a good way to show the travel-time data? Why or why not?*

Help them think about what they would have to do to make a line plot to display these data. You may even want to go through the process of trying to create a line plot. Fairly quickly, students will begin to see that the times these students take to travel to school vary from 5 to 60 minutes. It is difficult to make a line plot numbered 5 minutes, 6 minutes, 7 minutes, and so on, to show exact times. Also, the data are not really clustered by individual times, so it would be difficult to see any patterns in the data. A strategy in which the data are grouped is needed to help us look for patterns in the data.

   When students are familiar with the data, introduce the idea of making a stem-and-leaf plot to represent the data.

   The Student Edition outlines how to develop stem-and-leaf plots. However, we do not recommend that you have students read through this process on their own. Instead, we encourage you to present the process as a class exploration led by you. Students can consult the Student Edition for reference at a later time. Here is one way you may proceed.

- *Let's build a stem-and-leaf plot. When we look at our data, we see that the travel times vary from 5 minutes to 60 minutes. We can use this information to set up a graph that has a "stem" and several "leaves."*

- *The "leaves" are the units digits of the data values. The other digits in the data values form the stem. In this case, the stem is made up of the tens digits of the travel times.*

Suggested Questions You might ask these questions to review the idea of the tens digit:

- *Suppose a student takes 45 minutes to get to school. What is the tens digit?* (4)

- *What about 15 minutes?* (1)

- *What about 5 minutes?* (0)

- *What is the greatest tens digit we need to show?* (6)

- *We show the tens digits as a "stem" of numbers.*

```
0
1
2
3
4
5
6
```

- *Next, we begin to add "leaves" to the stem by placing each ones digit next to its tens digits. The first student has a travel time of 60 minutes. We show the ones digit (the 0) as a leaf.*

```
0
1
2
3
4
5
6 | 0
```

- *The next travel times are 15 minutes and 30 minutes. How should I add these to the graph?* (Put a 5 by the stem of 1, and 0 by the stem of 3.)

- *The next few travel times are 15 minutes, 15 minutes, 35 minutes, 15 minutes, 22 minutes, 25 minutes, and 20 minutes. Watch how I add these values to the graph.*

- *I would like you to work with a partner to copy this stem-and-leaf plot and to add the remaining leaves.*

```
0
1 | 5 5 5 5
2 | 2 5 0
3 | 0 5
4
5
6 | 0
```

Much of this problem's launch phase focuses on developing an understanding of the stem-and-leaf plot. The first step in this understanding is making a stem plot. Following this, students need to develop a better understanding of the idea that the data are now grouped in intervals and not simply as repeated values of the same measure. For example, 15 minutes is grouped with other data in the interval of 10–19.

Explore 2.1

Students will complete the stem-and-leaf plot in Question A. Notice that the leaves are not in ascending order. They are recorded as they occur in the data list.

Work with students on Question B to rearrange these leaves so they are in order. Transparency 2.1C shows the stem-and-leaf plot before and after arranging the data in ascending order. Help students to add a title to the stem plot and a key for interpreting the plot.

For Questions C and D, remind students as they select the interval to explain their reasoning. For Question E some students may have problems with finding the median. You can help these students by asking how finding the median on the stem-and-leaf plot is similar to finding the median when the data is represented in an ordered list. Check to see that all students are recording their strategies and are ready to explain them. Make note of the strategies you want to have students share in the Summary.

Summarize 2.1

Suggested Questions Ask questions that focus on reading the stem plot and on identifying intervals.

- *What is the shortest time for the 1 stem?* (10 min)

- *What is the longest time for the 1 stem?* (19 min)

- *What possible times are not shown for the 1 stem?* (12 min, 13 min, 14 min, 16 min, and 18 min)

- *We say that the interval of possible times for the 1 stem is from 10 to 19 minutes. What is the interval of possible times for the 0 stem?* (0–9 min)

- *What is the interval of possible times for the 2 stem?* (20–29 min)

- *What is the interval of possible times for the 3 stem?* (30–39 min)

Have pairs share their answers with the whole class. Make sure students explain the reasoning for their answers to Questions C and D. Also, make sure they explain their strategy for finding the median and range in Questions E and F.

The questions in this problem guide students to "read the data" and to "read between the data." Before you leave Problem 2.1, spend some time working with them to "read beyond the data."

- *How can we describe the shape of the data when they are grouped by tens?* (Most of the data cluster in one area of the stem from 0 min to 35 min. There are two outliers: 50 min and 60 min. Both these students take the bus and probably get on at the beginning of the bus route, since they live farther from the school than most of the other students.)

- *Using the mode probably won't tell us too much about the data with this graph. Why do you think this is so? Could we talk about an interval that contains the most data points?*

(The mode is the value in the data that occurs most frequently; in these data, the mode is 15 minutes. However, when we look at the stem plot, we are more interested in which interval(s) contain the most values. In these data, when the data are grouped by tens, the interval is 10–19 and it contains 17 values.)

- *How would we find the median for this set of data?* [There are 40 measures in this data set. The median is the number that marks the midpoint between the twentieth and twenty-first values. The second stem plot orders the data, so we can count from either end and locate the twentieth and twenty-first values (15 min and 17 min). Thus the median is 16 min.]

2.1 Traveling to School

Mathematical Goals

- Group numerical data in equal intervals and display their distribution using a stem-and-leaf plot
- Find measures of center and variation, including range and how data vary from the least to the greatest values, when a distribution is displayed using a stem-and-leaf plot

Launch

Display Transparencies 2.1A and 2.1B. Refer students to the table of data and the first two questions in the Getting Ready. Have them work on the questions for a few minutes before you have a whole-class discussion.

- *Look at the table of data. What are the three questions that the students asked to collect this data?*
- *Describe how you think they collected the data to answer each of these questions.*

Refer students to the third question in the Getting Ready.

- *Would a line plot be a good way to show the travel-time data? Why or why not?*

When students are familiar with the data, introduce the problem of making a stem-and-leaf plot to represent the data. The Student Edition outlines how to develop stem-and-leaf plots. We do not recommend that you have students read through this process on their own. Instead, we encourage you to present the process as a class exploration led by you. You may need to review the idea of the tens digit.

Materials

- Transparencies 2.1A–C
- Local street map (optional)

Vocabulary

- stem-and-leaf plot

Explore

Students will complete the stem-and-leaf plot in Question A. For Question B, work with students to rearrange these leaves so they are in order. Transparency 2.1C shows the stem and-leaf plot before and after arranging the data in ascending order. Help students add a title and key for the stem plot.

For Questions C and D, remind students as they select the interval to explain their reasoning. For Question E, some students may have trouble finding the median. You can help them by asking how finding the median on the stem-and-leaf plot is similar to finding the median when the data is represented in an ordered list. Check to see that all students are recording their strategies and are ready to explain them. Make note of the strategies you want to have students share in the Summary.

Ask questions that focus on reading the stem plot and on identifying intervals.

- *What is the shortest time for the 1 stem?*
- *What possible times are not shown for the 1 stem?*
- *We say that the interval of possible times for the 1 stem is from 10 to 19 minutes. What is the interval of possible times for the 0 stem?*

Have pairs share their answers with the whole class. Make sure students explain their reasoning. Before you leave Problem 2.1, spend some time working with them to "read beyond the data."

- *How can we describe the shape of the data when they are grouped by tens?*
- *Using the mode probably won't tell us too much about the data with this graph. Why do you think this is so? Could we talk about an interval that contains the most data points?*
- *How would we find the median for this set of data?*

Materials
- Student notebooks

ACE Assignment Guide for Problem 2.1

Core 1–4

Adapted For suggestions about adapting ACE exercises, see the CMP *Special Needs Handbook.*

Answers to Problem 2.1

A.

```
0 | 8 8 5 5 5 6
1 | 5 5 5 5 9 5 5 7 5 0 5 0 5 1 7 0 0
2 | 2 5 0 5 0 0 0 0 0 1
3 | 0 5 0 0 5
4 |
5 | 0
6 | 0
```

B.   Student Travel Times to School

```
0 | 5 5 5 6 8 8
1 | 0 0 0 0 1 5 5 5 5 5 5 5 5 5 7 7 9
2 | 0 0 0 0 0 0 1 2 5 5
3 | 0 0 0 5 5
4 |
5 | 0
6 | 0
```
Key: 2 | 5 means 25 min

C. Most students will reason that those students who have the shortest travel time (times in the 0–9 min interval) probably sleep the latest. However, because of other variables, times in the 10–19 min interval may be chosen.

D. Students who have longer travel times (the 50 min and 60 min outliers) probably get up the earliest.

E. 16 min; possible explanation: To find the median, count in from both ends of the plot until you reach the midpoint. It is between 15 and 17 min, so the median is 16 min.

F. 55 min; possible explanation: The range is the difference between the greatest value on the plot and the least value: $60 - 5 = 55$.

2.2 Jumping Rope

Goals

- Compare two distributions displayed using back-to-back stem-and-leaf plots
- Compare two distributions using statistics, such as median, range, and how the data vary from least to greatest values
- Identify outliers in a distribution

You may choose to investigate the problem using the data provided, or you may want to help your students conduct their own jump-rope activity and collect their own data. If your class conducts the activity, you will need to develop procedures for collecting the data. (Be aware that collecting these data is time-consuming!) You might ask the physical education teacher to help your students collect the data during their physical education class.

You may want to explore the problem using the data presented in the Student Edition and then extend the exploration phase to include your students' data, making comparisons where appropriate.

Launch 2.2

Present the problem by using Transparency 2.2 or by referring students to the Student Edition. Work with your students to make sure they can read the back-to-back stem plot before they begin to work on the problem. One way to do this is to cover the left side of the stem plot and ask students what information is shown on just the right side. Then cover the right side, and have students discuss how the data on the left side are read (when the stem is on the right). Finally, you can show both sets of data together, discussing how this arrangement lets you make comparisons between data sets.

Have students work in pairs or small groups.

Explore 2.2

Once students are comfortable with the data display, they can focus on the questions posed in Problem 2.2.

Suggested Questions For students who need support in answering Question A, ask:

- *What statistic might help you compare the class's jump roping?* (If necessary, remind them of the statistics that they talked about in Problem 2.1. For each statistic they mention, ask them why they chose this statistic and what it might tell them about the data. Try to have them realize that the median, how the data vary from the least to the greatest values, and range are very useful to compare data, and the mode may not be as useful.

- *How would you find that statistic using the data?* (Depending on the statistic they choose, you will need to ask them questions to help find the specific statistic they chose.)

Summarize 2.2

Hold a class discussion about Problem 2.2. The process of comparison may be difficult. Students may wonder how they can compare data sets that contain different numbers of data items. They may not immediately think about finding the medians, the least and greatest data values, and the ranges of the two classes' data, yet these are precisely the tools that can help them make comparative statements.

INVESTIGATION 2

2.2 Jumping Rope

Mathematical Goals

- Compare two distributions displayed using back-to-back stem-and-leaf plots
- Compare two distributions using statistics, such as median, range, and how the data vary from least to greatest values
- Identify outliers in a distribution

Launch

Present the problem by using Transparency 2.2 or by referring students to the Student Edition. Work with your students to make sure they can read the back-to-back stem plot before they begin to work on the problem. One way to do this is to cover the left side of the stem plot and ask students what information is shown on just the right side. Then cover the right side, and have students discuss how the data on the left side are read (when the stem is on the right). Finally, you can show both sets of data together, discussing how this arrangement lets you make comparisons between data sets.

Have students work in pairs or small groups.

Materials
- Transparency 2.2

Vocabulary
- outlier

Explore

Once students are comfortable with the data display, they can focus on the questions posed in Problem 2.2.

For students who need support in answering Question A, ask:

- *What statistic might help you compare the class's jump roping?*
- *How would you find that statistic using the data?*

Summarize

Hold a class discussion about Problem 2.2. The process of comparison may be difficult. Students may wonder how they can compare data sets that contain different numbers of data items. They may not immediately think about finding the medians, the least and greatest values, and the ranges of the two classes' data, yet these are precisely the tools that can help them make comparative statements.

Materials
- Student notebooks

ACE Assignment Guide for Problem 2.2

Core 5–7, 10, 13

Other *Extensions* 14; unassigned choices from previous problems

Adapted For suggestions about adapting ACE exercises, see the CMP *Special Needs Handbook*.

Answers to Problem 2.2

A. There are a variety of ways students can respond to this question. They may compute and compare the medians and the ranges, discuss the presence of outliers, or describe the shape of the data. The median number of jumps for Mrs. Reid's class is 28, with a range of $113 - 1 = 112$ jumps. The median number of jumps for Mr. Costo's class is 34, with a range of $300 - 1 = 299$ jumps. If the four outliers in Mr. Costo's class are ignored, the median number of jumps is 29, with a range of $104 - 1 = 103$ jumps. In the end, students need to give a well-developed response that makes their reasoning clear.

B. The two other outliers in Mr. Costo's class are both 160 jumps.

C. Possible answers: The students are physically fit, or the students jump rope frequently.

2.3 Relating Height to Arm Span

Goals

- Display distributions of paired-data values on coordinate graphs

- Explore relationships between paired-data values whose distributions are displayed using coordinate graphs

- Explore intervals for scaling the vertical axis (*y*-axis) and the horizontal axis (*x*-axis)

In their study of the process of data investigation your students have already developed many ways to represent data. It is important that they see why the techniques they have already mastered are not as effective as a coordinate graph for displaying the data for this problem. You may decide to propose alternative representations for the data to help your students understand why these representations do not help give the best representations of the distributions. Help your students begin to see the different strengths and weaknesses of the various forms of graphical representation.

Launch 2.3

Introduce coordinate graphs by using the Height and Arm Span data and graph. You can use Transparencies 2.3A and 2.3B to help you explain coordinate graphs and work through the questions of the Getting Ready. If you do not have an overhead projector, you could use a large sheet of grid paper, and label the axes as they appear in the Student Edition. Focus students on the axes, and discuss how they are labeled and scaled. Various students can locate the points of the sample data set by placing colored dots on the grid.

We suggest that the dots have initials on them to help students understand how to locate points. Be careful not to send the message that this is necessary when constructing coordinate graphs. On a graph of the entire class's data, initials would take up too much space and make it hard to read the graph and look for patterns.

When you feel students understand the example, talk about how to collect the class's data. Discuss strategies for how students can measure their heights and arm spans to the nearest inch (or centimeter). For example, students can mark their heights and arm spans on pieces of string and then measure the string with a yardstick or meter stick. Or they can tape yardsticks, meter sticks, or measuring tape to the wall and stand against them. Remind students that you are paying attention to accuracy and that they need to maintain consistency in their data-collection techniques with regard to such things as students' shoe heels.

- *Working with your partner, measure each other's height and arm span in inches (or centimeters). We will record our data in a central location so we can all see and use it.*

You may want to have students remove their shoes before measuring their heights. We have found that when students leave their shoes on, their height measurements are less accurate; that is, their heights are disproportionately greater than their arm spans. If students have trouble measuring accurately, affix a measuring tape to a wall vertically so students can stand against it, and affix another horizontally to a wall at shoulder height to help students measure their arm spans.

Use the board or a large sheet of grid paper to display the data. Have students write their names and record their two measures so these data may be seen by all students. You can organize your table of measures like the sample table in the Student Edition.

Once the data have been gathered and students are ready to work on organizing and interpreting it, bring the class back together to explain again that you are interested in how the two variables are, or seem to be, related. A coordinate graph is an ideal representation for analyzing the question. This is in fact the strength of coordinate graphs: showing how two variables are related.

INVESTIGATION 2

Suggested Question Consider asking:

• *How might we organize and display the data in a graph to help us answer the question?* [You could propose using a double bar graph, with two bars for each student—one showing arm span and the other showing height. Here's an example of a table of data and a double bar graph (Figure 1).]

Height and Arm Span Measures

Initials	Height (inches)	Arm Span (inches)
WE	63	60
AS	64	65
JF	64	65
AD	67	64
LP	68	68
JJ	69	67
GL	69	71
NY	70	68
BP	70	65
SH	70	73
CM	70	69
RS	71	70
KR	72	72
PL	73	75
JD	77	77

Help students see that the double bar graph representation is tedious to make because it requires many sets of bars. Because the data in the double bar graph are not grouped or ordered in any way, it is difficult to determine how to order the bars. However, you can see that the bars in each pair are about the same length, indicating a relationship between height and arm span.

You might also propose making a back-to-back stem plot with height on one side and arm span on the other.

Height and Arm Span Measures

Height		Arm Span
	5	
9 9 8 7 4 4 3	6	0 4 5 5 5 7 8 8 9
7 3 2 1 0 0 0 0	7	0 1 2 3 5 7
	8	

Key: 3|6|0 means 63 inches for height and 60 inches for arm span

This plot shows that the shape of both sets of data are similar, but we do not know which height is paired with which arm span. This makes it difficult to look for a relationship.

Ask your students to make a coordinate graph to display their class's data. Discuss how they might scale and label the axes.

Suggested Questions Here are some questions that students should consider (you may want to write these on the board):

• *Which measure should go on the horizontal axis and which should go on the vertical axis?* (Either is correct, but usually we put the measure we want to use to predict the other measure on the horizontal axis). NOTE: What measure students put on the axis will determine their answers to Question B parts (2) and (3).

Figure 1

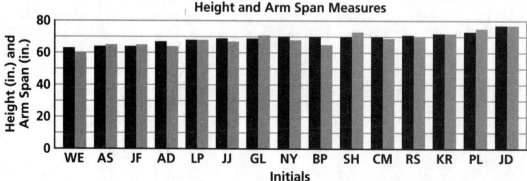

- *What are the least and greatest measures that you need to show on the horizontal axis? The vertical axis?* (Answers may vary, but will most likely fall from 50 to 80 in. for each axis.)

- *What would your graph look like if you just started each axis at 0?* (There would not be any data points from 0 to about 50 in.)

- *What labeling scheme will show all of the data in the space you have for the graph?* (Possible answer: The graph that covers the spread of measures, and is not scaled by ones.)

- *Will the scale you have chosen spread the data out too much or bunch it up so that it is hard to see patterns?* (Answers may vary. Try to help students see that scaling by large numbers (20) or small numbers (1) may make patterns hard to see.)

When you feel your students have a good idea about what scales make sense, allow them to make the graph and to answer the questions in the problem. Arrange students in small groups for the exploration.

Explore 2.3

Observe students as they make their coordinate graphs. For those students who are having trouble constructing the coordinate graph, go over the answers to the questions in the launch. Students struggling with Question A may need to refer to some points on the graph to get an idea of a reasonable answer. For students struggling with Question B, ask them what the coordinates of a specific point below the line represent, and what the coordinates for a specific point above the line

represent. Ask them to generalize from these specific points, what other points above or below the line represent.

Summarize 2.3

Let groups share their graphs and tell how they chose the scale or labeling scheme for each axis. Discuss which graphs seem to show the data best and why.

Discuss the answers to Question B. Help students understand what the three different regions of the graph represent. When height is on the horizontal axis and arm span is on the vertical axis, the line represents points where height equals arm span, the region above the line represents points where arm span is greater than height, and the region below the line represents points where height is greater than arm span. Here is an example of a coordinate graph for height and arm span data:

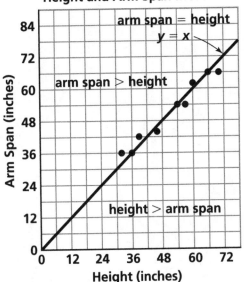

Height and Arm Span Measures

2.3 Relating Height to Arm Span

Mathematical Goals

- Display distributions of paired-data values on coordinate graphs
- Explore relationships between paired-data values whose distributions are displayed using coordinate graphs
- Explore intervals for scaling the vertical axis (*y*-axis) and the horizontal axis (*x*-axis)

Launch

Introduce coordinate graphs by using the Height and Arm Span data and graph. You can use Transparencies 2.3A and 2.3B to help you explain coordinate graphs and work through the questions of the Getting Ready. Focus students on the axes, and discuss how they are labeled and scaled.

When you feel students understand the example, talk about how to collect the class's data. Discuss strategies for how students can measure their heights and arm spans to the nearest inch (or centimeter).

- *Working with your partner, measure each other's height and arm span in inches (or centimeters). We will record our data in a central location so we can all see and use it.*

Have students write their names and record their two measures so these data may be seen by all students. Bring the class back together to explain again that you are interested in how the two variables are, or seem to be, related. Consider asking:

- *How might we organize and display the data in a graph to help us answer the question?*

Ask your students to make a coordinate graph to display their class's data. Here are some questions that students should consider:

- *Which measure should go on the horizontal axis and which should go on the vertical axis?*
- *What is the spread of measures that you need to show on the horizontal axis? The vertical axis?*
- *What would your graph look like if you just started each axis at 0?*
- *What labeling scheme will show all of the data in the space you have for the graph?*

When you feel your students have a good idea about what scales make sense, allow them to make the graph and to answer the questions in the problem. Arrange students in small groups for the exploration.

Materials
- Transparencies 2.3A, 2.3B
- Large grid paper (optional)

Vocabulary
- coordinate graph
- *x*-axis
- *y*-axis

Observe students as they make their coordinate graphs. For those students who are having trouble constructing the coordinate graph, go over the answers to the questions in the launch. Students struggling with Question A may need to refer to some points on the graph to get an idea of a reasonable answer. For students struggling with Question B, ask them what the coordinates of a specific point below the line represent, and what the coordinates for a specific point above the line represent. Ask them to generalize, from these specific points, what other points above or below the line represent.

Materials
- Yardsticks (or meter sticks or tape measure)
- Large grid paper (optional)
- String (optional)

Summarize

Let groups share their graphs and tell how they chose the scale or labeling scheme for each axis. Discuss which graphs seem to show the data best and why.

Discuss the answers to Question B. Help students understand what the three different regions of the graph represent. See extended Teacher's Guide for completed coordinate graph.

Materials
- Student notebooks

ACE Assignment Guide for Problem 2.3

Core 8, 11

Other unassigned choices from previous problems

Adapted For suggestions about adapting Exercise 8 and other ACE exercises, see the CMP *Special Needs Handbook*.

Connecting to Prior Units 12: *Bits and Pieces I*

Answers to Problem 2.3

A. Data and graph depend on your class's data. If you know the measure of a person's arm span, you can reasonably guess that the person's height is approximately the same. Some students may say that the measure of a person's height may be the same as or slightly above or below the measure of a person's arm span.

B. The line is the graph of $y = x$. Students do not need to understand this equation now. Instead, focus on understanding what students know about the data that are located on, above, or below the line.

1. Answer depends on your class's data. They should understand that points on the line represent students whose heights are equal to their arm spans.

2. Answer depends on your class's data. Points below the line represent students whose height is greater than their arm span (when height is on the horizontal axis and arm span on the vertical axis).

3. Answer depends on your class's data. Points above the line represent students whose arm span is greater than their height (when height is on the horizontal axis and arm span on the vertical axis).

2.4 Relating Travel Time to Distance

Goals

- Explore relationships between paired-data values whose distributions are displayed using coordinate graphs
- Explore intervals for scaling the vertical axis (*y*-axis) and the horizontal axis (*x*-axis)

The value of a coordinate graph is that it can show a relationship between different sets of data. Students may easily agree that there must be some kind of relationship between distance and time of travel. On the other hand, they can see there is no realistic relationship between travel time and favorite pet.

Launch 2.4

In this problem, students use the data introduced in Problem 2.1.

- *In the last problem, you were introduced to coordinate graphs. These graphs are useful because they allow us to look at two sets of data at the same time, so we can find relationships between them.*

Display Transparency 2.4. Spend time discussing the scales for each axis so students understand how the axes relate to the data in the table. You might choose to recreate the graph on a large sheet of grid paper. This will allow students to better understand how the graph was created before they spend time discussing what it tells them. You could have various students locate the points by placing colored stick-on dots on the grid paper or by making a dot on the transparency grid with a marker.

Have students work individually or in pairs.

Explore 2.4

Give each student a copy of Labsheet 2.4. Make sure students are writing their justification for their answer to Question B about the relationship between the time required to travel to school and distance traveled. For Question C, help students focus on what each of the coordinates represent in the ordered pairs. Some students may need to locate these points on the graph before they try to answer this question. For those students struggling with Question D, ask them to start to draw a graph labeling it with the same scale and use it to think about their answers.

Summarize 2.4

Suggested Questions Refocus students on the big question:

- *Suppose you know how long it takes a particular student to travel to school. Do you know anything about that student's distance from school?*

Let several students or pairs read their justifications. This may raise an opportunity to ask such questions as the following:

- *Look at the axis showing time. How can you tell from the graph the shortest time it took someone to travel to school?* (the data point that aligns vertically with the shortest time: 5 min)

- *How can you tell the longest time?* (the data point that aligns vertically with the longest time: 60 min)

- *Look at the axis showing distance. How can you tell from the graph the shortest distance it took someone to travel to school?* (the data point that aligns horizontally with the shortest distance: 0.25 mi)

- *How can you tell the longest distance?* (the data point that aligns horizontally with the longest distance: 4.75 mi)

Discuss the answers to Questions C and D. These questions help deepen students' understanding of the data displayed on the graph.

INVESTIGATION 2

2.4 Relating Travel Time to Distance

Mathematical Goals

- Explore relationships between paired-data values whose distributions are displayed using coordinate graphs
- Explore intervals for scaling the vertical axis (*y*-axis) and the horizontal axis (*x*-axis)

Launch

In this problem, students use the data introduced in Problem 2.1.

- *In the last problem, you were introduced to coordinate graphs. These graphs are useful because they allow us to look at two sets of data at the same time, so we can find relationships between them.*

Display Transparency 2.4. Spend time discussing the scales for each axis so students understand how the axes relate to the data in the table. You might choose to recreate the graph on a large sheet of grid paper. This will allow students to better understand how the graph was created before they spend time discussing what it tells them. You could have various students locate the points by placing colored stick-on dots on the grid paper or by making a dot on the transparency grid with a marker.

Have students work individually or in pairs.

Materials
- Transparency 2.4
- Large grid paper (optional)
- colored stick-on dots (optional)

Explore

Give each student a copy of Labsheet 2.4. Make sure students are writing their justification for their answer to Question B about the relationship between the time required to travel to school and distance traveled.

For Question C, help students focus on what each of the coordinates represent in the ordered pairs. Some students may need to locate these points on the graph before they try to answer this question. For those students struggling with Question D, ask them to start to draw a graph labeling it with the same scale and use it to think about their answers.

Materials
- Labsheets 2.4, 2ACE Exercise 15 (1 per student)

Summarize

Refocus students on the big question:

- *Suppose you know how long it takes a particular student to travel to school. Do you know anything about that student's distance from school?*

Let several students or pairs read their justifications. This may raise an opportunity to ask such questions as the following:

- *Look at the axis showing time. How can you tell from the graph the shortest time it took someone to travel to school? How can you tell the longest time?*

Materials
- Student notebooks

continued on next page

Summarize *continued*

- *Look at the axis showing distance. How can you tell from the graph the shortest distance it took someone to travel to school? How can you tell the longest distance?*

Discuss the answers to Questions C and D. These questions help deepen students' understanding of the data displayed on the graph.

ACE Assignment Guide for Problem 2.4

Differentiated Instruction
Solutions for All Learners

Core 12
Other *Applications* 9, *Extensions* 15; unassigned choices from previous problems
A copy of Labsheet 2ACE Exercise 15 can help students with Exercise 15.

Adapted For suggestions about adapting ACE exercises, see the CMP *Special Needs Handbook*.
Connecting to Prior Units 11: *Bits and Pieces I*

Answers to Problem 2.4

A.

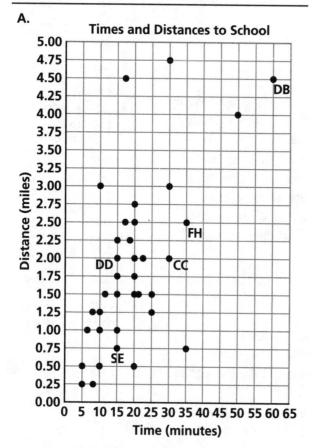

B. The graph seems to go up in distance as time increases. So students who live farther away from school generally spend more time getting to school. But you must also consider how students get to school (e.g., walking, by car, or by bus).

C. 1. These students live the same distance from school, but one takes an hour to get to school, and the other takes only 17 min. Maybe one goes by car and one by bus. Or perhaps, both go by bus, but one is picked up earlier on the route.

2. These three students take the same time to get to school, but live very different distances from school. Maybe one walks, one takes a bus, and one travels by car.

3. These students have different travel times and live approximately the same distance from school.

D. 1. The axes are labeled with different scales because the distance and time are measured in different increments. Distance is in quarter miles and time is in intervals of 5 min. The spread of times is from 5 min to 60 min, but the spread of distances is only from $\frac{1}{4}$ mi to $4\frac{3}{4}$ mi.

2. If we used the scale from the time axis on the distance axis, all the points would be on top of each other. If we used the scale from the distance axis on the time axis, the graph would not fit on a piece of paper.

The student edition pages for this investigation begin on the next page.

Notes _____
_____
_____
_____

Using Graphs to Explore Data

Sometimes data may be spread out. When these data are displayed on a line plot or a bar graph, it is not easy to see patterns. In this investigation, you will learn how to highlight data using displays called stem-and-leaf plots and back-to-back stem-and-leaf plots to help you see patterns.

In Investigation 1, you analyzed single sets of data. Sometimes you may want to analyze whether there is a relationship between two different data sets. In this investigation, you will learn how to display data pairs from two different data sets using a coordinate graph.

2.1 Traveling to School

While investigating the times they got up in the morning, a middle-school class was surprised to find that two students got up almost an hour earlier than their classmates. These students said they got up early because it took them a long time to get to school. The class then wondered how much time it took each student to travel to school. The data they collected are on the next page.

Getting Ready for Problem 2.1

Use the table on the next page to answer these questions:

- What three questions did the students ask?
- How might the students have collected the travel-time data?
- Would a line plot be a good way to show the data? Why or why not?

30 Data About Us

Notes _____

_____

_____

_____

Times and Distances to School

Student's Initials	Time (minutes)	Distance (miles)	Mode of Travel
DB	60	4.50	Bus
DD	15	2.00	Bus
CC	30	2.00	Bus
FH	35	2.50	Bus
SE	15	0.75	Car
AE	15	1.00	Bus
CL	15	1.00	Bus
LM	22	2.00	Bus
QN	25	1.50	Bus
MP	20	1.50	Bus
AP	25	1.25	Bus
AP	19	2.25	Bus
HCP	15	1.50	Bus
KR	8	0.25	Walking
NS	8	1.25	Car
LS	5	0.50	Bus
AT	20	2.75	Bus
JW	15	1.50	Bus
DW	17	2.50	Bus
SW	15	2.00	Car
NW	10	0.50	Walking
JW	20	0.50	Walking
CW	15	2.25	Bus
BA	30	3.00	Bus
JB	20	2.50	Bus
AB	50	4.00	Bus
BB	30	4.75	Bus
MB	20	2.00	Bus
RC	10	1.25	Bus
CD	5	0.25	Walking
ME	5	0.50	Bus
CF	20	1.75	Bus
KG	15	1.75	Bus
TH	11	1.50	Bus
EL	6	1.00	Car
KLD	35	0.75	Bus
MN	17	4.50	Bus
JO	10	3.00	Car
RP	21	1.50	Bus
ER	10	1.00	Bus

Investigation 2 Using Graphs to Explore Data   **31**

Notes

The students decide to make a stem-and-leaf plot of the travel times.

A **stem-and-leaf plot** looks like a vertical stem with leaves to the right of it. It is sometimes simply called a *stem plot*.

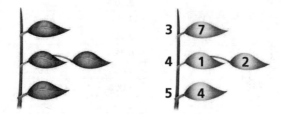

To make a stem plot to represent travel times, separate each data value into a left "stem" and a right "leaf."

For these data, the "stem" will be the tens digits. Because the travel times include values from 5 minutes to 60 minutes, the stem will be the digits 0, 1, 2, 3, 4, 5, and 6.

- Make a vertical list of the tens digits in order from least to greatest.

- Draw a line to the right of the digits to separate the stem from the "leaves."

10's 1's

```
0 |
1 |
2 |
3 |
4 |
5 |
6 |
```

The "leaves" will be the ones digits. For each data value, add a leaf next to the appropriate tens digit on the stem.

- The first data value is 60 minutes. Write a 0 next to the stem of 6.

- The next value is 15 minutes. Write a 5 next to the stem of 1.

- The travel times of 30 and 35 minutes are shown by a 0 and 5 next to the stem of 3.

```
0 |
1 | 5
2 |
3 | 0 5
4 |
5 |
6 | 0
```

32   Data About Us

Notes _____

_____

_____

_____

Problem 2.1 Making a Stem-and-Leaf Plot

A. Use the Travel to School data to make the stem plot. The plot is started for you.

```
0 |
1 | 5 5 5 5 9
2 | 2 5 0
3 | 0 5
4 |
5 |
6 | 0
```

B. Now redraw the stem plot, putting the data in each leaf in order from least to greatest. Include a title for your plot. Also include a key like the following that tells how to read the plot.

> Key
> 2 | 5 means 25 minutes

C. Which students probably get to sleep the latest in the morning? Why do you think this?

D. Which students probably get up the earliest? Why do you think this?

E. What is the median of the travel-time data? Explain how you found this.

F. What is the range of the travel-time data? Explain.

ACE Homework starts on page 40.

Investigation 2 Using Graphs to Explore Data   **33**

Notes _____

_____

_____

_____

Mrs. Reid's class competed against Mr. Costo's class in a jump-rope contest. Each student jumped as many times as possible. Another student counted the jumps and recorded the total. The classes made the *back-to-back stem plot* shown to display their data. Look at this plot carefully. Try to figure out how to read it.

When the two classes compare their results, they disagree about which class did better.

- Mr. Costo's class says that the range of their data is much greater.

- Mrs. Reid's class says this is only because they had one person who jumped many more times than anybody else.

- Mrs. Reid's class claims that most of them jumped more times than most of the students in Mr. Costo's class.

- Mr. Costo's class argues that even if they do not count the person with 300 jumps, they still did better.

Number of Jumps

Mrs. Reid's class		Mr. Costo's class
8 7 7 7 5 1 1	0	1 1 2 3 4 5 8 8
6 1 1	1	0 7
9 7 6 3 0 0	2	3 7 8
7 6 5 3	3	0 3 5
5 0	4	2 7 8
	5	0 2 3
2	6	0 8
	7	
9 8 0	8	
6 3 1	9	
	10	2 4
3	11	
	12	
	13	
	14	
	15	1
	16	0 0
	17	
	18	
	19	
	20	
	21	
	22	
	23	
	24	
	25	
	26	
	27	
	28	
	29	
	30	0

Key: 7 | 3 | 0 means 37 jumps for Mrs. Reid's class and 30 jumps for Mr. Costo's class

Notes

_____

_____

_____

_____

Problem 2.2 Comparing Distributions

A. Which class did better overall in the jump-rope contest? Use what you know about statistics to help you justify your answer.

B. In Mr. Costo's class, there are some very large numbers of jumps. For example, one student jumped 151 times, and another student jumped 300 times. We call these data outliers. **Outliers** are data values that are located far from the rest of the other values in a set of data. Find two other outliers in the data for Mr. Costo's class.

C. An outlier may be a value that was recorded incorrectly, or it may be a signal that something special is happening. All the values recorded for Mr. Costo's class are correct. What might account for the few students who jumped many more times than their classmates?

ACE **Homework starts on page 40.**

Investigation 2 Using Graphs to Explore Data   **35**

Notes _____

_____

_____

_____

In earlier problems, you worked with one measure at a time. For example, you looked at the number of letters in students' names and travel times to school. In this problem, you will look at the relationship between two different counts or measures.

If you look around at your classmates, you might guess that taller people have wider arm spans. But is there *really* any relationship between a person's height and his or her arm span? The best way to find out more about this question is to collect some data.

Here are data on height and arm span (measured from fingertip to fingertip) that one class collected.

Height and Arm Span Measurements

Initials	Height (inches)	Arm Span (inches)
NY	63	60
JJ	69	67
CM	73	75
PL	77	77
BP	64	65
AS	67	64
KR	58	58

Notes _____

_____

_____

_____

You can show two different data values at the same time on a **coordinate graph.** Each point on a coordinate graph represents two data values. The horizontal axis, or **x-axis**, represents one data value. The vertical axis, or **y-axis**, represents a second data value. The graph below shows data for height along the x-axis and data for arm span along the y-axis. Each point on the graph represents the height and the arm span for one student.

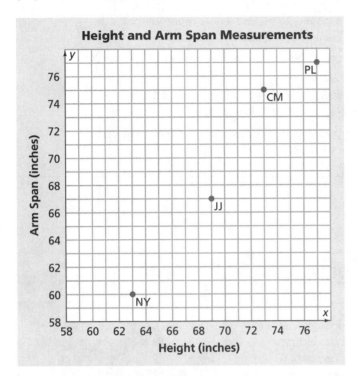

Study the table of data on the previous page and the coordinate graph. Four points have already been plotted and labeled with the students' initials. The location of each point is shown in the table at the right.

Initials	Point
NY	(63, 60)
JJ	(69, 67)
CM	(73, 75)
PL	(77, 77)

Getting Ready for Problem

- Where would you place the points and initials for the remaining three people?
- Why do the axes of the graph start at (58, 58)?
- What would the graph look like if the axes started at (0, 0)?

Notes _____

_____

_____

_____

Problem 2.3 Making and Reading Coordinate Graphs

Collect the height and arm span data of each person in your class. Make a coordinate graph of your data. Use the graph to answer the questions.

A. If you know the measure of a person's arm span, do you know his or her height? Explain.

B. Draw a diagonal line on the graph that would represent points at which arm span and height are equal.

1. How many data points lie on this line? How does arm span relate to height for the points *on* the line?

2. How many data points lie below this line? How does arm span relate to height for the points *below* the line?

3. How many data points lie above this line? How does arm span relate to height for the points *above* the line?

ACE **Homework starts on page 40.**

2.4 Relating Travel Time to Distance

In Problem 2.1, you made stem-and-leaf plots to show data about travel times to school. You can use the same data to look at the relationship between travel time and distance from home to school on a coordinate graph.

38 Data About Us

Notes _____

_____

_____

_____

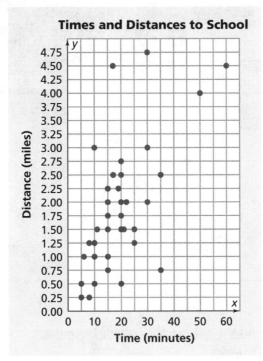

Times and Distances to School

Problem 2.4 Using Coordinate Graphs to Find Relationships

Study the graph above and the data from Problem 2.1.

active math
online
For: Statistical Tool
Visit: PHSchool.com
Web Code: amd-8204

A. Copy the coordinate graph. Mark and label a point with the student's initial for the first five students in the table.

B. If you know a student's travel time, what do you know about that student's distance from school? Use the graph to justify your answer.

C. Locate each set of points on the coordinate graph. What can you tell about travel time and distance from school for the students these points represent?

  1. (17, 4.50) and (60, 4.50)

  2. (30, 2.00), (30, 3.00), and (30, 4.75)

  3. (17, 4.50) and (30, 4.75)

D. 1. Why do the axes have different scales?

  2. What would the graph look like if both axes used the same scales?

ACE Homework starts on page 40.

Investigation 2 Using Graphs to Explore Data **39**

Notes _____

_____

_____

_____

Applications

For Exercises 1–4, use the stem-and-leaf plot at the right.

Student Travel Times to School

0	3 3 5 7 8 9
1	0 2 3 5 6 6 8 9
2	0 1 3 3 3 5 5 8 8
3	0 5
4	5

Key: 2 | 5 means 25 min

1. **Multiple Choice** How many students spent 10 minutes traveling to school?

   A. 1   **B.** 9   **C.** 10   **D.** 19

2. **Multiple Choice** How many students spent 15 minutes or more traveling to school?

   F. 10   **G.** 16   **H.** 17   **J.** 25

3. How many students are in the class? Explain.

4. What is the typical time it took these students to travel to school? Explain.

For Exercises 5–8, use the table on the next page.

5. Make a stem-and-leaf plot of the students' ages. The plot has been started for you at the right. Notice that the first value in the stem is 6, because there are no values less than 60 months.

6. What ages, in years, does the interval of 80–89 months represent?

7. What is the median age of these students?

8. **a.** On a piece of grid paper, make a coordinate graph. Show age (in months) on the horizontal axis and height (in centimeters) on the vertical axis. To help you choose a scale for each axis, look at the least and greatest values for each measure.

   b. Explain how you can use your graph to find out whether the youngest student is also the shortest student.

6
7
8
9
10
11
12
13
14
15

40   Data About Us

Notes _____

_____

_____

_____

c. Use your graph to describe what happens to students' heights as the students get older.

d. What would happen to the graph if you extended it to include people in their late teens or early twenties? Explain.

Student Ages, Heights, and Foot Lengths

Age (mo)	Height (cm)	Foot Length (cm)	Age (mo)	Height (cm)	Foot Length (cm)
76	126	24	148	164	26
73	117	24	140	152	22
68	112	17	114	135	20
78	123	22	108	135	22
81	117	20	105	147	22
82	122	23	113	138	22
80	130	22	120	141	20
90	127	21	120	146	24
101	127	21	132	147	23
99	124	21	132	155	21
103	130	20	129	141	22
101	134	21	138	161	28
145	172	32	152	156	30
146	163	27	149	157	27
144	158	25	132	150	25

Notes _____

_____

_____

_____

9. The coordinate graph below shows the height and foot length data from the table on the previous page. Notice that the scale on the *x*-axis uses intervals of 5 centimeters and the scale on the *y*-axis uses intervals of 1 centimeter.

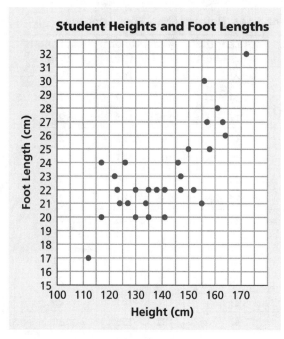

a. If you know a person's foot length, can you tell that person's height? Explain.

b. Find the median height and the median foot length. The median height is about how many times the median foot length?

c. Measure the length of your foot in centimeters. Your height is about how many times your foot length?

d. Look at your responses to parts (b) and (c). How can you use this information to answer part (a)? Explain.

e. What would the graph look like if you started each axis at 0?

Notes _____

_____

_____

_____

Connections

10. a. Use the data in the Student Ages, Heights, and Foot Lengths table from Exercises 5–8. Make a stem-and-leaf plot of the students' heights.

b. Describe how to make a line plot of the students' heights. What are the least and greatest data values? How does this help you make the line plot?

c. Describe how to make a bar graph of the students' heights. What are the least and greatest data values? How does this help you make the graph?

d. Why might you display these data using a stem-and-leaf plot instead of a line plot or a bar graph?

11. The table below shows some of the Student Ages, Heights, and Foot Lengths data in centimeters. The table includes two new columns. Copy and complete the table to show heights and foot lengths in meters.

Homework
Help Online
PHSchool.com
For: Help with Exercise 11
Web Code: ame-8211

a. Round the height for each student to the nearest tenth of a meter.

b. Make a line plot showing these rounded height data.

c. What is the typical height for these students in meters? Explain.

Student Ages, Heights, and Foot Lengths

Age (mo)	Height (cm)	Height (m)	Foot Length (cm)	Foot Length (m)
76	126	■	24	■
73	117	■	24	■
68	112	■	17	■
78	123	■	22	■
81	117	■	20	■
82	122	■	23	■
80	130	■	22	■
90	127	■	21	■
138	161	■	28	■
152	156	■	30	■
149	157	■	27	■
132	150	■	25	■

Investigation 2 Using Graphs to Explore Data   **43**

Notes _____

_____

_____

_____

12. The pie chart shows the portion of time Harold spent on homework in each subject last week.

Time Spent on Homework

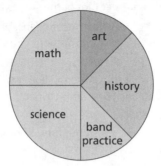

a. If Harold spent two hours on math homework, about how many hours did he spend on homework altogether?

b. About what percent of his time did Harold spend on math, science, and history homework? Explain.

Extensions

For Exercises 13 and 14, use the jump-rope data on the next page.

13. Make a back-to-back stem-and-leaf plot that compares either the girls in Mrs. Reid's class with the girls in Mr. Costo's class or the boys in Mrs. Reid's class with the boys in Mr. Costo's class. Did the girls (or boys) in one class do better than the girls (or boys) in the other class? Explain your reasoning.

14. Make a back-to-back stem-and-leaf plot that compares the girls in both classes with the boys in both classes. Did the girls do better than the boys? Explain.

44   Data About Us

Notes

Number of Jumps

Mrs. Reid's Class Data		Mr. Costo's Class Data	
Boy	5	Boy	1
Boy	35	Boy	30
Girl	91	Boy	28
Boy	62	Boy	10
Girl	96	Girl	27
Girl	23	Girl	102
Boy	16	Boy	47
Boy	1	Boy	8
Boy	8	Girl	160
Boy	11	Girl	23
Girl	93	Boy	17
Girl	27	Boy	2
Girl	88	Girl	68
Boy	26	Boy	50
Boy	7	Girl	151
Boy	7	Boy	60
Boy	1	Boy	5
Boy	40	Girl	52
Boy	7	Girl	4
Boy	20	Girl	35
Girl	20	Boy	160
Girl	89	Boy	1
Boy	29	Boy	3
Boy	11	Boy	8
Boy	113	Girl	48
Boy	33	Boy	42
Girl	45	Boy	33
Girl	80	Girl	300
Boy	36	Girl	104
Girl	37	Girl	53

Investigation 2 Using Graphs to Explore Data   **45**

Notes _____

_____

_____

_____

15. A group of students challenged each other to see who could come the closest to guessing the number of seeds in his or her pumpkin. The data they collected are shown in the table and the graph.

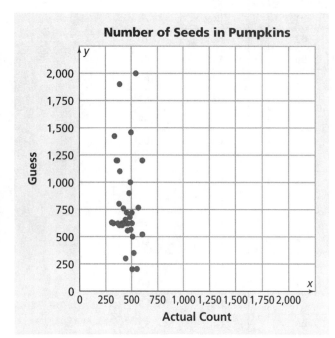

Number of Seeds in Pumpkins

Guess	Actual
630	309
621	446
801	381
720	505
1,900	387
1,423	336
621	325
1,200	365
622	410
1,000	492
1,200	607
1,458	498
350	523
621	467
759	423
900	479
500	512
521	606
564	494
655	441
722	455
202	553
621	367
300	442
200	507
556	462
604	384
2,000	545
1,200	354
766	568
624	506
680	486
605	408
1,100	387

Notes _____

_____

_____

_____

a. What do you notice about how the actual counts vary? What are the median and the least and greatest values of the actual counts?

b. What do you notice about how the guesses vary? What are the median and the least and greatest values of the guesses?

c. Make your own coordinate graph of the data. Draw a diagonal line on the graph to connect the points (0, 0), (250, 250), (500, 500), all the way to (2,250, 2,250).

d. What is true about the guesses compared to the actual counts for points near the line you drew?

e. What is true about the guesses compared to the actual counts for points above the line?

f. What is true about the guesses compared to the actual counts for points below the line?

g. In general, did the students make good guesses? Use what you know about median and range to explain your reasoning.

h. The scales on the axes are the same, but the data are bunched together. How would you change the scale to show the data points better?

Investigation 2 Using Graphs to Explore Data **47**

Notes _____

_____

_____

_____

Mathematical Reflections 2

In this investigation, you learned how to make stem-and-leaf plots as a way to group a set of data so you can study its shape. You have also learned how to make and read coordinate graphs. Coordinate graphs let you examine two things at once so you can look for relationships between them. The following questions will help you summarize what you have learned.

Think about your answers to these questions. Discuss your ideas with other students and your teacher. Then write a summary of your findings in your notebook.

1. Describe how to locate the median and range using a stem plot.

2. When you make a coordinate graph of data pairs, how do you determine where to place each point?

3. What do you consider when choosing a scale for each axis of a coordinate graph?

4. Numerical data can be displayed using more than one kind of graph. How do you decide when to use a line plot, a bar graph, a stem-and-leaf plot, or a coordinate graph?

Unit Project   What's Next?

Think about the survey you will be conducting about middle-school students. What kinds of questions can you ask that might involve using a stem-and-leaf plot to display the data? Can you sort your data into two groups and use a back-to-back stem plot to help you compare the data?

Notes _____

_____

_____

_____

Investigation 2

ACE
Assignment Choices

Problem 2.1
Core 1–4

Problem 2.2
Core 5–7, 10, 13
Other *Extensions* 14; unassigned choices from previous problems

Problem 2.3
Core 8, 11
Other unassigned choices from previous problems

Problem 2.4
Core 12
Other *Applications* 9, *Extensions* 15; unassigned choices from previous problems

Adapted For suggestions about adapting Exercise 8 and other ACE exercises, see the CMP *Special Needs Handbook*.
Connecting to Prior Units 11, 12: *Bits and Pieces I*

Applications

1. A

2. H

3. 26 students; you can count the number of leaves on the stem plot. Each value represents one student.

4. Answers will vary. Students may find the median, which is 18.5 min. They may offer other alternatives as well; however, they must provide clear reasoning for their responses.

5.
Student Ages

6	8
7	3 6 8
8	0 1 2
9	0 9
10	1 1 3 5 8
11	3 4
12	0 0 9
13	2 2 2 8
14	0 4 5 6 8 9
15	2

Key: 7 | 6 means 76 months

6. 6.7 to 7.4 yr, or about $6\frac{1}{2}$ to $7\frac{1}{2}$ yr; divide the number of months by 12 to convert to years.

7. $113\frac{1}{2}$ mo (about $9\frac{1}{2}$ yr); there are 30 data values, so the median is the value halfway between the fifteenth and sixteenth values (113 and 114).

8. a. (Figure 2)

   b. You can locate the youngest student (the furthest to the left on the horizontal axis) and the shortest student (the closest to the bottom on the vertical axis). You can quickly see that the youngest student is the shortest student.

   c. In general, as students get older, their heights increase.

   d. People stop growing in their late teens or early twenties. The graph would level out at this time, and we would not see much increase afterward.

9. a. The graph indicates that, in general, taller people have longer foot lengths. However, knowing a person's foot length will not definitively tell you that person's height.

   b. The median height is 141 cm. (NOTE: If students use the table they will find a median height of $139\frac{1}{2}$ cm. This is because the graph takes the heights of only

29 students out of the 30 students on the table. Only one student with the height of 127 cm and the foot length of 21 cm is represented on the graph). The median foot length is 22 cm. Dividing 141 by 22, we see that the median height is a little more than 6.4 times the median foot length.

   c. Answers will vary. Height is generally about 6 to $6\frac{1}{2}$ times foot length.

   d. The answers to parts (b) and (c) show that a person's height is generally 6 to $6\frac{1}{2}$ times his or her foot length, so we can use foot length to estimate height. However, we cannot know the exact height for certain.

   e. If you started the graph at 0, the data points would be shifted horizontally to the right about 20 spaces and vertically upward about 14 spaces. There would be no data points in the lower left-hand region of the graph.

Figure 2

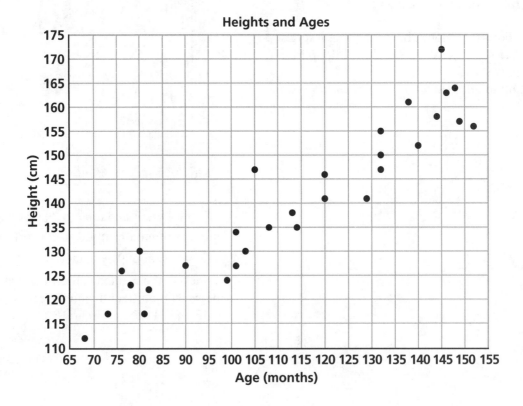

Connections

10. a.

Student Heights

```
11 | 2 7 7
12 | 2 3 4 6 7 7
13 | 0 0 4 5 5 8
14 | 1 1 6 7 7
15 | 0 2 5 6 7 8
16 | 1 3 4
17 | 2
```
Key: 13 | 5 means 135 centimeters

b. The least value is 112, and the greatest value is 172. These points give us the endpoints with which you can begin and end your line plot. To complete your line plot, put an X over each value in the line plot that is found in the data.

c. The least value is 112, and the greatest value is 172. These values give us the endpoints with which you can begin and end your bar graph. To complete your bar graph, make a bar over each value in the bar graph whose height aligns with the frequency of those values.

d. By making a stem-and-leaf plot, you do not have to draw a bar for each height, so the stem-and-leaf plot is more compact.

11. a. (Figure 3)

b.

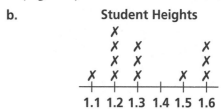

Student Heights

c. Some students may say that the median of 1.3 meters is typical.

12. a. 8 hours

b. 75%; according to the pie chart, Harold spends about 2 hours on math, 2 hours on science, and 2 hours on history. So he spends $2 + 2 + 2$, or 6 out of 8 hours on those subjects altogether. $\frac{6}{8} = 75\%$

Figure 3

Student Heights and Foot Lengths

Age (mo)	Height (cm)	Height (m)	Rounded Height (tenth of a meter)	Foot Length (cm)	Foot Length (m)
76	126	1.26	1.3	24	0.24
73	117	1.17	1.2	24	0.24
68	112	1.12	1.1	17	0.17
78	123	1.23	1.2	22	0.22
81	117	1.17	1.2	20	0.20
82	122	1.22	1.2	23	0.23
80	130	1.30	1.3	22	0.22
90	127	1.27	1.3	21	0.21
138	161	1.61	1.6	28	0.28
152	156	1.56	1.6	30	0.30
149	157	1.57	1.6	27	0.27
132	150	1.50	1.5	25	0.25

Extensions

13. The graph below (Figure 4) uses G and B in place of actual numbers of jumps (refer to earlier stem plot for numbers), giving girls' and boys' data on the same plot. Students will have made separate plots, but you may use this summary graph as a way to show how we can modify stem plots to give different information.

Generally speaking, girls performed slightly better in Mr. Costo's class than the girls in Mrs. Reid's class. It seems as though Mr. Costo's class has three outliers for girls. One girl in

Mr. Costo's class jumped rope more times than anyone else in either class. The boys performed similarly in both classes. We can see an outlier for boys in each class.

14. One way to answer this question is to show all the girls' data on one side of the stem plot and all the boys' data on the other side, as shown below. (Figure 5)

The boys' data clusters at the lower end of the stem plot. The girls' data is spread out with more of the data showing larger numbers of jumps. So the girls did better.

Figure 4

Number of Jumps

Mrs. Reid's Class		Mr. Costo's Class
B B B B B B B	0	B B B B G B B B
B B B	1	B B
B G B G B G	2	G G B
G B B B	3	B B G
G B	4	B B G
	5	B G G
B	6	B G
	7	
G G G	8	
G G G	9	
	10	G G
B	11	
	12	
	13	
	14	
	15	G
	16	G B
	17	
	18	
	19	
	20	
	21	
	22	
	23	
	24	
	25	
	26	
	27	
	28	
	29	
	30	G

Figure 5

Number of Jumps

Girls		Boys
4	0	1 1 1 1 2 3 5 5 7 7 7 8 8 8
	1	0 1 1 6 7
7 7 3 3 0	2	0 6 8 9
7 5	3	0 3 3 5 6
8 5	4	0 2 7
3 2	5	0
8	6	0 2
	7	
9 8 0	8	
6 3 1	9	
4 2	10	
	11	3
	12	
	13	
	14	
1	15	
0	16	0
	17	
	18	
	19	
	20	
	21	
	22	
	23	
	24	
	25	
	26	
	27	
	28	
	29	
0	30	

15. a. The actual counts vary from 309 to 607 seeds, so the range is 298 seeds. The graph shows that the actual counts fall within a smaller range compared to the guesses. The median is $458\frac{1}{2}$ seeds (halfway between 455 and 462).

b. The guesses vary from 200 to 2,000 seeds, so the range is 1,800 seeds. The graph shows that the guesses are much more spread out than the actual counts. The median is $642\frac{1}{2}$ seeds (halfway between 630 and 655).

c. (Figure 6)

d. Points on or near the line represent guesses that are very close or equal to the actual counts.

e. Points above the line represent guesses that are larger than the actual counts.

f. Points below the line represent guesses that are smaller than the actual counts.

g. In general, the guesses are larger than the actual counts. The median for the guesses is $642\frac{1}{2}$ with a range of 1,800 seeds. The median of the actual counts is $458\frac{1}{2}$ with a range of 298 seeds. The median for the actual counts is much smaller than the median for the guesses. The range for the guesses spans $1,800 \div 298$, or about 6 times as many values.

h. Possible answer: You could change the scale on the horizontal axis to go from 0 to 750 scaling by 100.

Possible Answers to Mathematical Reflections

1. These can easily be found on the stem plot. Find the median by first determining the number of data values in the data set and then finding half of that number. For example, if there are 46 data values, the median lies between the twenty-third and twenty-fourth values. If there are 45 data values, the median is the twenty-third value. As long as you count consecutively from the least value or the greatest value, you may count from either end of the data displayed in the stem plot to locate the median. Find the range by arranging all leaves in ascending order and then finding the difference between the greatest and least values in the data set.

Figure 6

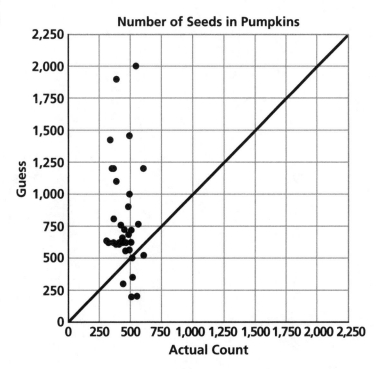

Number of Seeds in Pumpkins

2. To place a point, start at $(0, 0)$ and move to the right, along the horizontal axis (x-axis), the number of units given by the first coordinate. Then move up, along the vertical axis (y-axis), the number of units given by the second coordinate.

3. You assign the first measure for each pair to the x-axis, and the second measure to the y-axis. Then, you consider the spread of the data as you set up the scale of each axis.

4. A stem-and-leaf plot is more useful than a line plot or bar graph for data that are spread out. For this type of data, grouping by intervals allows us to see patterns in the data. Line plots are quickly constructed graphs that can be used when you want to "sketch" a data set. If there is a great number of data items, the bar graph is a more useful tool because its vertical scale is adjustable.

Investigation 3

What Do We Mean by *Mean*?

Mathematical and Problem-Solving Goals

- Understand the mean as a number that "evens out" or "balances" a distribution
- Create distributions with designated means
- Recognize that data with the same mean may have different distributions
- Reason with a model that clarifies the development of the algorithm for finding the mean
- Experiment with how the mean, as a measure of center, responds to changes in the number and magnitude of data values

Research has shown that students can learn the algorithm for finding the mean with relative ease. This investigation focuses on the development of an understanding of what the mean represents and what it tells us about a set of data. The notions of "evening out" and "balancing" a distribution at a point (the mean) on the horizontal axis are modeled by using cubes and stick-on notes. These models support the development of the algorithm for finding the mean: adding up all the numbers and dividing by the total number of numbers.

Summary of Problems

Problem 3.1 Finding the Mean

Students find the mean of a set of data by the evening-out method and then look for more efficient methods.

Problem 3.2 Data With the Same Mean

Students explore the idea that different sets of data may yield the same mean.

Problem 3.3 Using the Mean

Students explore what happens to the mean when outliers or clusters of values at one end or the other of a distribution are added to a data set.

Mathematics Background

For background on measures of center, see pages 7 and 8.

	Suggested Pacing	Materials for Students	Materials for Teachers	ACE Assignments
All	4 days	Calculators, blank transparencies and transparency markers (optional), student notebooks, large sheets of unlined paper	Blank transparencies and transparency markers	
3.1	$1\frac{1}{2}$ days	Cubes (10 each of 6 different colors per group), stick-on notes	Transparencies 3.1A and 3.1B	1–4, 7, 8, 19
3.2	1 day	Cubes (10 each of 6 different colors per group), stick-on notes	Transparencies 3.2A and 3.2B, cubes (10 each of 6 different colors)	5, 6, 10, 20, 21
3.3	1 day		Transparencies 3.3A and 3.3B	9, 11–18, 22, 23
MR	$\frac{1}{2}$ day			

Finding the Mean

Goal

- Understand the mean as a number that "evens out" or "balances" a distribution

Provide pairs of students with cubes and stick-on notes.

Launch 3.1

The U.S. Census is a survey that seeks to count the number of people living in the United States and to describe key characteristics about these people, such as household size.

Suggested Questions Ask about the census.

- *Does anyone know what the purpose of the U.S. Census is?* (Historically, the purpose of the census is to count the number of people living in the United States. This is done to compute the number of representatives each state will have in the U.S. House of Representatives.)

- *The Census Bureau has developed a definition of who to count. The census focuses on counting the people who live in households rather than asking questions like "How many people are in your family?"*

- *The word* household *refers to all the people who live in a "housing unit," which may be a house, an apartment, some other group of rooms, or a single room, like a room in a boarding house.*

- *Why do you think the census asks: "How many people are in your household?" and not "How many people are in your family?"* (By defining the word *household* as it does, the census seeks to eliminate confusion about who to count. Only the people who live in a household and use that location as their permanent address at the time the census is taken are counted as members of that household. When you try to define the word *family*, you run into a lot of questions about who to count: "What if I have an older sister who doesn't live with us now?" "Can I count my grandmother?" The census must follow a single rule about who to count. The definition of *household* helps census takers to report population data accurately.)

Data Exploration Opportunity

If you have time, you may want to gather data about students' household sizes from your class. You can use this problem framework:

A. Use the definition of *household* from the U.S. Census. How many people are in your household?

B. Collect household size data from everyone in your class.

C. Make a display to show the distribution of the data.

D. What is the mean number of people in your class's households? Explain how you found your answer.

Use the Getting Ready to launch Problem 3.1. Have students construct the physical model in small groups by building a stack of cubes for each student's household. Each stack should be a single color and different from the colors of the other stacks (this way, you can refer to "Ossie the orange stack," "Ruth the red stack," or "Arlene the blue stack"). The stacks should look something like this:

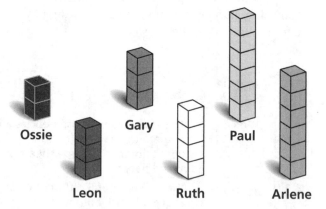

Have the groups arrange their cube stacks in order from shortest to tallest.

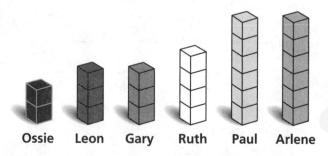

- *What is the median of these data?* (the midpoint between 3 and 4, or 3.5 people)

- *What is the mode of these data?* (The data is bimodal. The two modes are 3 and 6.)

- *You can find the average of these data by "evening out" the number of cubes in each stack.*

Have the students try this on their own. After students have had a few minutes to work with their stacks, have a class discussion about what they found out. The stacks are "evened out" by moving cubes from taller stacks to shorter stacks. Since each stack was originally a single color, students will be able to see from which stacks the "moved data" came.

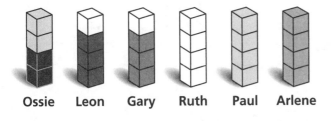

| Ossie | Leon | Gary | Ruth | Paul | Arlene |

- *How many cubes are in each stack?* (4)

- *When you moved the cubes to even out the stacks, the stacks for households with fewer than four people were made taller, and the stacks for households with more than four people were made shorter.*
  You moved two cubes from each of the two stacks with six cubes. So you decreased the stack heights by a total of four cubes. (Write 2 + 2 = 4 on the board.)
  You added two cubes to the stack with two cubes, and you added one cube to each of the two stacks with three cubes. So you increased the stack heights by a total of four cubes. (Write 2 + 1 + 1 on the board.)

Students will be able to see these changes by observing where the colors ended up after the evening out was completed.

- *The amount of increase was the same as the amount of decrease. We can say that each household has an average of four people. Another way to say this is that there are, on average, four people per household. Some of the households (Paul's and Arlene's) actually have more than four people; their extra cubes have been moved to households with fewer than four people (Ossie's, Leon's, and Gary's). One household (Ruth's) already had four people, so none of her cubes were moved.*

- *The average, or "evened out," stack height you found equals the mean number of people in a household. What is the mean number of people in a household?* (4)

Explore 3.1

As you move around the room, help pairs to understand that they need to build six stacks, one stack for each of the six students, with the numbers of cubes representing the members of each household. Suggest that they build the stacks for each person with the same color cube.

Summarize 3.1

Discuss each of the questions in Problem 3.1, encouraging students to share their strategies for solving the problem. They need to justify their strategies by explaining why what they did works. Most students will use the strategy of evening out the cubes to find the mean, but they may use other strategies as well. These strategies may include showing the mean as a balance point in the distribution using a line plot (see Launch 3.2), or using the standard algorithm of adding up all of the people in each household and dividing that total by the number of households. If the standard algorithm is mentioned as a strategy, ask students to discuss how it is similar to the other strategies of "evening out" the cubes or "balancing" the stick-on notes in the line plot.

Going Further

In section 3.1, students worked with sets of data from six households. Each set of data had the same total number of people. Once they have focused on how the mean develops, you may want to investigate other sets of data that have larger numbers of data values. Have students do the same set of explorations they did for Problem 3.1, but with data sets that involve eight households, each having a mean of four people.

The data sets are linked to representations using line plots. As cube stacks, the data remain ungrouped. Once a line plot is made, the data are grouped and show the frequency of occurrence of each data value.

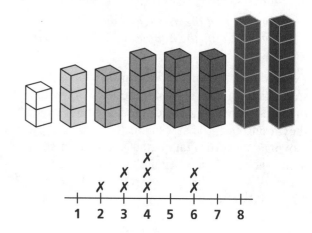

Data Set A

Data Set B

Data Set C

Data Set D

Evening out the stacks can be mirrored by making adjustments on the line plot that reflect the changes in the heights of the stacks:

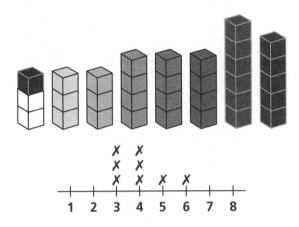

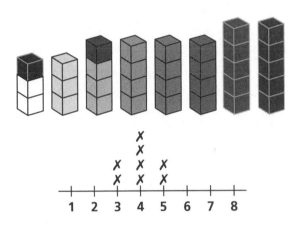

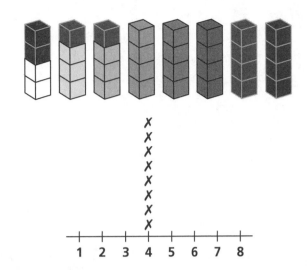

The mean may be visualized as the "evened out" number, either represented by a number of stacks all the same height or a line plot with all the data values the same. Once students explore these small data sets, they are encouraged to develop numerical strategies to determine the mean for large data sets.

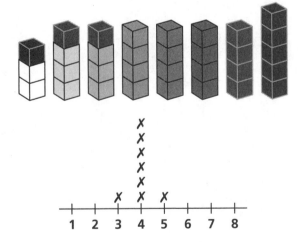

3.1 Finding the Mean

PACING $1\frac{1}{2}$ days

Mathematical Goal

- Understand the mean as a number that "evens out" or "balances" a distribution

Launch

Use the Getting Ready to launch Problem 3.1. Have students construct the physical model in small groups by building a stack of cubes for each student's household. Each stack should be a single color and different from the colors of the other stacks. Have the groups arrange their cube stacks in order from shortest to tallest.

- *What is the median of these data?*
- *What is the mode of these data?*
- *You can find the average of these data by "evening out" the number of cubes in each stack.*

Have the students try this on their own.

- *How many cubes are in each stack?*
- *The average, or "evened out," height you found equals the mean number of people in a household. What is the mean number of people in a household?*

Materials
- Transparencies 3.1A, 3.1B
- Cubes (10 each of 6 different colors per pair)

Explore

As you move around the room, help pairs to understand that they need to build six stacks, one stack for each of the six students, with the numbers of cubes representing the members of each household. Suggest that they build the stacks for each person with the same color cube.

Materials
- Stick-on notes
- Large sheets of unlined paper

Summarize

Discuss each of the questions in Problem 3.1, encouraging students to share their strategies for solving the problem. They need to justify their strategies by explaining why what they did works.

Most students will use the strategy of "evening out" the cubes to find the mean, but they may use other strategies as well. These strategies may include showing the mean as a balance point in the distribution using a line plot, or using the standard algorithm of adding up all of the people in each household and dividing that total by the number of households. If the standard algorithm is mentioned as a strategy, ask students to discuss how it is similar to the other strategies of "evening out" the cubes or "balancing" the stick-on notes in the line plot.

Materials
- Student notebooks

Going Further

See the extended Summarize section.

ACE Assignment Guide
for Problem 3.1

Core 1–4
Other *Connections* 7, 8, 19

Adapted For suggestions about adapting
ACE exercises, see the CMP *Special Needs Handbook*.
Connecting to Prior Units 7, 8: *Bits and Pieces I*

Answers to Problem 3.1

A.

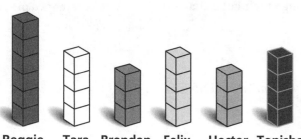

Reggie Tara Brendan Felix Hector Tonisha

  1. 24; Possible answer: count the total number
  of cubes.

  2. 4; Possible answer: If you "even out" the
  stacks, there are four cubes in each stack.

  3. The means are the same.

B. Possible answers: Use stick-on notes to make
a line plot. Then "even out" the notes. Some
students may notice in this problem that the
mean is the sum of all the people in the
households divided by the number of
households; or rather, the sum of the data
divided by the number of data values.

Data With the Same Mean

Goals

- Create distributions with designated means

- Recognize that data with the same mean may have different distributions

- Reason with a model that clarifies the development of the algorithm for finding the mean

   In this problem, students create data sets with a given number of households and a given mean. They discover that it is possible for different data sets to have the same mean.

Launch 3.2

Suggested Questions Display Transparency 3.2A and ask this question:

- *Look at the two line plots. How are these distributions alike? How are they different?* (Possible answers: They have the same mean. The spread of the data are different.)

Introduce the line-plot representation.

- *Using stick-on notes and a number line, let's now make a line plot to show these data.*

   Rebuild the original cube stacks. Begin to build the line plot by indicating that the first person, Ossie, has a two-person household, so one stick-on note is placed above the 2 on the line plot. Work back and forth between the cube representation and the line-plot representation to complete the model.

Numbers of People in Households

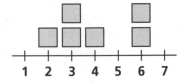

Suggested Questions Students may not easily see that the cube stacks and the line plot display the same information. Help them to explore the models by asking such questions as these:

- *Looking at the stacks, how many households are shown?* (6)

- *Looking at the line plot, how many households are shown?* (6)

- *Looking at the stacks, how many people are in the six households altogether?* (24)

- *How did you figure this out?* (by counting the number of cubes)

- *How should the number of people represented by the line plot compare to the number of people represented by the stacks?* (It should be the same, as it was built using the data from the stacks.)

- *How can you verify your thinking?*

   Help students understand how to compute the total number of people from the line plot: the stick-on note above the 2 means one household of two people, or a total of two people; the two stick-on notes above the 3 mean two households of three people, or a total of six people; and so on.

   The concept that a stick-on note above a numeral on the line plot represents that number of people in one household is an important concept for students to grasp that may need to be carefully considered. With the cube model, each stack represents the number of people in a household, so the cubes make it easier for students to visualize how to count the total number of people.

   Show the top portion of Transparency 3.2B.

- *Here is our line plot. The arrow points to the mean. You can think of the line plot as balancing on the arrow.*

Numbers of People in Households

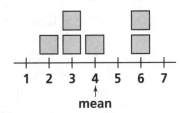

mean

- *To even out the values, we take 2 cubes away from each data value of 6 cubes. This leaves us with three cube stacks, each with a height of 4 cubes. This makes our distribution out of balance.*

INVESTIGATION 3

Reveal the second graph on Transparency 3.2B.

Numbers of People in Households

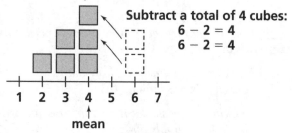

Subtract a total of 4 cubes:
6 − 2 = 4
6 − 2 = 4

- *To balance the distribution, we need to increase the heights of the data values of 2 cubes and 3 cubes to make each of them up to a height of 4 cubes.*

Show the third graph on Transparency 3.2B.

- *By comparing the equations next to each line plot, you can see that the total number of cubes you subtract is the same as the total number of cubes you add.*

Numbers of People in Households

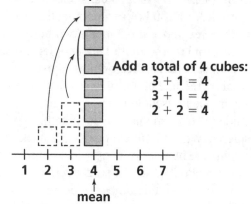

Add a total of 4 cubes:
3 + 1 = 4
3 + 1 = 4
2 + 2 = 4

- *Our cube stacks let us even out the numbers in each household to find the mean. Now we see how the "evened out" households appear on our line plot. We say the mean is a kind of a balance point to the distribution.*

Have students try to write a definition of the term *mean* in their notebooks. Based on their work here, students may say something like "The mean is the value when we have evened out the data values so they are all the same value." Their definitions may be vague now. You will return to this task in Problem 3.3.

Ask students the questions in the Getting Ready:

- *How many households are there in each situation?* (6)

- *What is the total number of people in each situation?* (24)

- *How do these facts relate to the mean in each case?* (Students will notice that the distributions look different and that the data values are different. However, they both show 6 households with a total of 24 people. Thus, they both have a mean of 4 people. Some students may observe that dividing 24 people among 6 households is 4 people per household.)

Propose the idea of having additional data sets with the same mean.

- *Do you think it is possible to have other sets of data about 6 households that are different from the ones we explored and still have a mean of 4 people?* (Hopefully, students will think this is possible. Some may not agree; some may not know. Challenge students to work with you to make a new distribution with 6 households and a mean of 4 people.)

- *Our data set must have a total of six households. Suppose that the first household had three people. I can show these three people by making a stack of three cubes.*

Make a stack of three cubes of the same color.

- *How many more stacks do I need to make to show the remaining households?* (5)

- *Now, suppose another household has eight people. I'll make a stack of eight cubes to represent that household.*

Using a different color, make a stack of eight cubes.

- *How many people are represented with just the two stacks we've made?* (11)

- *What do you think I should do next?*

Some students may see that the goal is to have a total of 24 people in the 6 households and that, since you have accounted for 11 people, the remaining 4 households must have 13 people altogether. As you construct each new stack, students will need to count how many more of the 24 people have been accounted for. Be patient with this discussion. Once you have a set of six stacks, you may want to make a line plot and then check for a mean of 4 by evening out the stacks. If the mean is not 4, discuss with students what you need to do to the data set so that the mean will be 4.

Have pairs work on Problem 3.2.

For Question A, if students are having problems finding a data set with a mean of 4 people per household, encourage them to explore through trial and error. If pairs are still having trouble, suggest they work backwards moving from six stacks of 4 cubes to six stacks with different number of cubes in each. As you observe the pairs working, make sure they create a line-plot distribution with stick-on notes. Do a quick check as you scan their line plots. The total number of people represented must be 24.

Once students have found a successful strategy for Question A, they can use the same strategy for Questions B and C. Although the strategies used for Questions A through C will work for Question D, students may struggle with the idea of a "half" of a person. Explain to students that the mean of $3\frac{1}{2}$ people does not have to be an actual or possible value in the data set. If students struggling with making the line plot use a trial and error strategy, you could help them by asking them the possible spread for this data set to create the line plot. You can also ask them to think about their reasons for placing the stick-on notes where they do. You can observe them create their first line plot, and ask them to determine if it has a mean of $3\frac{1}{2}$. If it does not have a mean of $3\frac{1}{2}$, ask them how close it is to $3\frac{1}{2}$ and what they might change in the line plot to obtain this mean number of people per household. After they make their changes, check that their line plots still represent six students' households. Another possibility is to ask students how many total people are in these six students' households and then ask them to create a line plot that illustrates six households with that same total of people. All students will have a chance to work through their reasoning for Question D as they share their work in the Summary.

Summarize 3.2

In the Summary you will want to draw out from students their understanding that

1. for Questions A–D, there can be different distributions with the same mean.

2. among the different problems that have different means, there is a similar way in which they go about making a distribution with their respective means.

3. another strategy for finding the mean is to add up all the values and divide by the number of values. This algorithm will come from the work they have done in the investigation with the cubes and line plots in finding the mean.

Suggested Questions Have each pair display one line plot for Question A. Ask students to look at the displays for Question A.

- *Are any of the distributions the same?*

- *How many different distributions are posted?*

- *Is it possible to have different distributions with the same mean?*

Point to specific examples, and ask questions about them.

- *How many households are represented?* (6)

- *How many people are there in all the households?* (24; make sure students compute this number)

- *What is the mean?* (4)

Discuss Questions B–D as thoroughly as you did Question A. Post distributions, and ask the same questions about the number of households, the total number of people, and the mean.

You will want to help students synthesize what they know about making distributions with different means. Ask questions that help them focus their observations on identifying common strategies.

- *What are some quick ways to come up with different sets of data with 6 households and a mean of 4 people?*

- *What are some quick ways to come up with different sets of data with 7 households and a mean of 4 people?*

- *What are some quick ways to come up with different sets of data with 7 households and a mean of 3 people?*

- *What are some quick ways to come up with different sets of data with 6 households and a mean of $3\frac{1}{2}$ people?*

Ideally, students will see that if they know the number of households and the mean number of people in the households, they can determine the total number of people in all of the households. Using this total, they can work backward to create a data set showing the total number of people distributed among the households.

- *How can you use what you know about the number of people in all the households and the number of households to find the mean number of people?*

Students have used the number of households and the mean to determine the total number of people:

Known: number of households, mean number of people

Unknown: total number of people

Now, we want them to use an algorithm that involves the number of households and the total number of people to find the mean:

Known: number of households, total number of people

Unknown: mean number of people

Pose an example:

- *Suppose there are 6 households with a total of 36 people. What is the mean number of people in each household?*

Have students use cubes to build six stacks representing the possible numbers of people in each household. Work with them as they even out the stacks to find the mean. Can they answer your original question now? Then, ask them to find the mean in a different way.

- *How can you determine the mean without using cubes?* (Some students may visualize distributing 36 cubes evenly among the six households. This is like 36 ÷ 6. Other students may use the example of the evened-out cubes, noting that the total number of people and households stay the same; you just have to share the cubes among all the households. Students may suggest other strategies.)

Give more examples:

- *There are 12 students with a total of 60 people in their households. How would we go about finding the mean number of people in each household? What is the mean number of people in each household? (5) Why does your strategy work?*

Help students define an algorithm for finding the mean:

The mean of a set of data is determined by adding up the data values and dividing by the number of data values.

3.2 Data With the Same Mean

Mathematical Goals

- Create distributions with designated means
- Recognize that data with the same mean may have different distributions
- Reason with a model that clarifies the development of the algorithm for finding the mean

Launch

Display Transparency 3.2A.

- *Look at the two line plots. How are these distributions alike? How are these different?*

Ask students the questions in the Getting Ready. Propose the idea of having additional data sets with the same mean.

Discuss additional sets with the same mean using the cubes and the line plot. Be patient with this discussion. Have pairs work on Problem 3.2.

Materials
- Transparencies 3.2A, 3.2B
- Stick-on notes
- Cubes (10 each of 6 different colors)

Explore

For Question A, if students are having problems finding a data set with a mean of 4 people per household, encourage them to use trial and error. If pairs still have trouble, suggest working backwards moving from six stacks of 4 cubes to 6 stacks with different numbers of cubes in each. Make sure pairs create a line plot with stick-on notes. Students can use their successful strategy for Question A in B and C. For D, students may struggle with the idea of a "half" of a person. Explain that the mean of $3\frac{1}{2}$ people does not have to be an actual or possible value in the data set.

Materials
- Cubes (10 each of 6 different colors per pair)
- Stick-on notes
- Large sheets of unlined paper

Summarize

Ask students questions while looking at the displays for Question A.

- *Are any of the distributions the same?*
- *How many different distributions are posted?*
- *Is it possible to have different distributions with the same mean?*

Discuss Questions B–D thoroughly. Ask questions that help them focus on identifying common strategies:

- *How can you use the number of people in all the households and the number of households to find the mean number of people?*

Pose an example:

- *Suppose there are 6 households with a total of 36 people. What is the mean number of people in each household?*

Ask them to find the mean in different ways. Give more examples. Help students define an algorithm for finding the mean.

Materials
- Student notebooks

ACE Assignment Guide
for Problem 3.2

Core 5, 10
Other *Applications* 6; *Extensions* 20, 21; unassigned choices from previous problems

Adapted For suggestions about adapting Exercise 6 and other ACE exercises, see the CMP *Special Needs Handbook*.
Connecting to Prior Units 10: *Bits and Pieces I*

Answers to Problem 3.2

A. Possible line plots:

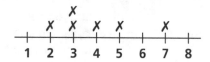

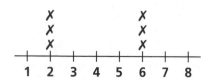

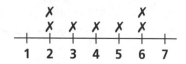

B. Possible line plots:

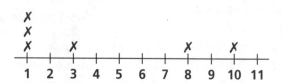

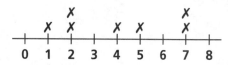

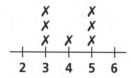

C. Possible line plots:

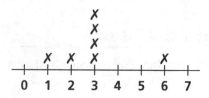

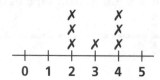

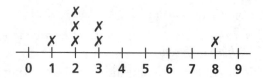

D. 1. Possible line plots:

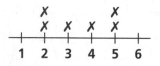

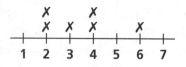

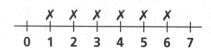

2. The mean is the number obtained by dividing the sum of the data values equally among the households. Unlike the mode, the mean does not have to be an actual (or possible) value in the data set, so the mean can be $3\frac{1}{2}$.

3. The mean is not a whole number if the number of data values does not evenly divide the sum of the data values. For example, in Question D, part (1), the sum of the data is 21, but the number of data values is 6. Since 6 does not divide 21 evenly, the mean will not be a whole number.

3.3 Using the Mean

Goal

- Experiment with how the mean, as a measure of center, responds to changes in the number and magnitude of data values

   This problem will broaden students' understanding of the mean by focusing on how data values may affect the mean. Students explore what happens to the mean when additional data values are added. These additional values may be outliers or within the data spread but toward one end or the other of the distribution.

Launch 3.3

The data used in this problem were collected from a group of middle school students who answered this question:
   How many movies did you watch last month?

Suggested Question

- *How would you answer this question: How many movies did you watch last month? What do we mean by a movie?*

   There are some misunderstandings about what "movie" means in this context. It seems the students responding to the survey thought of "movie" as being any kind of video or television movie they watched during the previous month. Discuss possible ways students might interpret what is being asked. Your students might want to think about the mean number of movies watched per day. For example, the student who watched 15 movies in one month averaged $\frac{1}{2}$ movie per day (if a month is considered 30 days).

   Have pairs work together to complete the problem.

Explore 3.3

Check to see that for each part of Problem 3.3 students continuously add the new values of movies watched. In other words, they are not starting over with the original data set each time and then adding the new values. For Question B,

when adding 31 to the stem plot, check to see that students are adding the stem of 3. Remind students to explain what they observe is happening to the mean in Questions B and C. For students struggling with Question D, ask them to reason part (1) by using what happened to the mean in Question B as an example when they added 31 movies. Ask them to reason part (2) by what happened to the mean in Question C when those values were added to the data.

Summarize 3.3

Suggested Questions Begin the discussion by asking students the following questions:

- *What was the mean number of movies in Question A?* (9)

- *In Question B, a student whose data value is much greater than the rest of the data is added. What happened to the mean?* (It is greater than the mean in Question A.)

- *In general, what effect do you think outliers have on the mean of a data set? Why?* (Outliers can pull the mean down or up depending on how large or small they are.)

- *In Question C, several students' data were added. They clustered near the lower end of the distribution, but were not outliers. Because there are several lower values, they still affect the mean. Let's test our ideas on our data.*

- *What data values could you add to cause the mean of the 9 movies to increase?* (values that are greater than 9)

- *What data values could you add to cause the mean of 9 movies to decrease?* (values that are less than 9)

- *What data values could you add to cause the mean of 9 movies to remain the same?* (values that are less than 9 paired with values that are greater than 9—the number above the 9 and the number below the 9 need to be equidistant from the 9 to keep the mean at 9, along with any values that equal 9)

3.3 Using the Mean

Mathematical Goal

- Experiment with how the mean, as a measure of center, responds to changes in the number and magnitude of data values

Launch

The data used in this problem were collected from a group of middle school students who answered this question: How many movies did you watch last month? Consider asking:

- *How would you answer this question: How many movies did you watch last month? What do we mean by a movie?*

There are some misunderstandings about what "movie" means in this context. Discuss possible ways students might interpret what is being asked. Your students might want to think about the mean number of movies watched per day. Have pairs work together to complete the problem.

Materials
- Transparencies 3.3A, 3.3B

Explore

Check to see that for each part of Problem 3.3 students continuously add the new values of movies watched. For Question B, when adding 31 to the stem plot, check to see that students are adding the stem of 3. Remind students to explain what they observe is happening to the mean in Questions B and C. For students struggling with Question D, ask them to reason part (1) by using what happened to the mean in Question B as an example when they added 31 movies. Ask them to reason part (2) by what happened to the mean in Question C when those values were added to the data.

Materials
- Large sheets of unlined paper

Summarize

Begin the discussion by asking students the following questions:

- *What was the mean number of movies in Question A?*
- *In Question B, a student whose data value is much greater than the rest of the data is added. What happened to the mean?*
- *In general, what effect do you think outliers have on the mean of a data set? Why?*
- *In Question C, several students' data were added. They clustered near the lower end of the distribution, but were not outliers. Because there are several lower values, they still affect the mean. Let's test our ideas on our data.*
- *What data values could you add to cause the mean of the 9 movies to increase?*
- *What data values could you add to cause the mean of 9 movies to decrease?*
- *What data values could you add to cause the mean of 9 movies to remain the same?*

Materials
- Student notebooks

ACE Assignment Guide for Problem 3.3

Differentiated Instruction
Solutions for All Learners

Core 11, 17, 23
Other *Connections* 9, 12–16, 18; *Extensions* 22; unassigned choices from previous problems

Adapted For suggestions about adapting ACE exercises, see the CMP *Special Needs Handbook*.
Connecting to Prior Units 12–16: *Bits and Pieces I*

Answers to Problem 3.3

A. 1. The total number of students is 10.

2. The total number of movies watched is 90.

3. The mean number of movies watched is 9.

B. 1. When 31 is added to the stem plot, there is a gap between 18 and 31 movies watched.

Movies Watched

0	3 3 5 6 6 7
1	1 5 6 8
2	
3	1

Key: 1 | 5 means 15 movies

2. Yes, because it is much greater than the other values in the data set.

3. The new mean is 11 movies.

4. The mean for Question A is 9, and the new mean for Question B is 11. The mean for Question B is greater than the mean for the data in Question A. Because 31 is a much greater number of movies watched than the values that were in Question A, it increases the mean.

C. 1. The eight new values increase the number of values in the 0–9 interval.

Movies Watched

0	2 2 3 3 4 4 4 5 5 5 5 6 6 7
1	1 5 6 8
2	
3	1

Key: 1 | 5 means 15 movies

2. The new data values are not outliers because they fall where the data were already clustered in the 0–9 interval.

3. The new mean is about 8 movies.

4. The new mean is less than the mean in Questions A (9) and Question B (11). The mean has decreased from the mean of 11 movies in Question B because the 8 new values cluster at the low end of the data set.

D. 1. Adding outliers to the data set can greatly affect the mean. Adding much greater numbers "pulls" the mean up (increases it), and adding much smaller numbers pulls the mean down (decreases it).

2. Adding data values that cluster near one end of the data affects the mean by "pulling" it in the direction of the data added.

3. These changes occur because increases (or decreases) in data values, when added to the sum of all the data values and divided by the number of data values result in a quotient (mean) that is greater (less) than the mean before the new data values were included.

Investigation 3

What Do We Mean by *Mean*?

The main use of the United States Census is to find out how many people live in the United States. The census provides useful information about household size. In the census, the term *household* means all the people who live in a "housing unit" (such as a house, an apartment, or a room of a boarding house).

In earlier investigations, you used median and mode to describe a set of data. Another measure of center is the *mean*. It is the most commonly used measure of center for numerical data. Another word often used to indicate the mean of a set of data is *average*.

Notes _____

_____

_____

_____

Finding the Mean

Six students in a middle-school class use the United States Census guidelines to find the number of people in their household. Each student then makes a stack of cubes to show the number of people in his or her household.

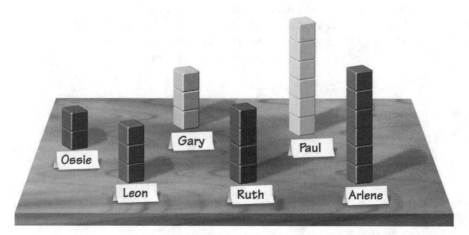

You can see from the stacks that the six households vary in size.

Getting Ready for Problem 3.1

Use cubes and make stacks like the ones shown above. Use the stacks to answer these questions:

- What is the median of these data?
- What is the mode of these data?

Make the stacks all the same height by moving cubes.

- How many cubes are in each stack?
- The average stack height you found represents the mean number of people in a household. What is the mean number of people in a household?

STUDENT PAGE

Notes _____

_____

_____

_____

Another group of students made the table below.

Household Size

Name	Number of People
Reggie	6
Tara	4
Brendan	3
Felix	4
Hector	3
Tonisha	4

A. Make stacks of cubes to show the size of each household.

   1. How many people are in the six households altogether? Explain.

   2. What is the mean number of people per household? Explain.

   3. How does the mean for these data compare to the mean for the data in the Getting Ready?

B. What are some ways to determine the mean number of a set of data other than using cubes?

ACE Homework starts on page 56.

Investigation 3 What Do We Mean by *Mean*?   **51**

Notes _____

_____

_____

_____

3.2 Data With the Same Mean

The line plots below show two different distributions with the same mean.

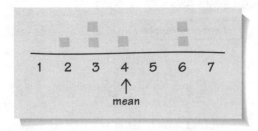

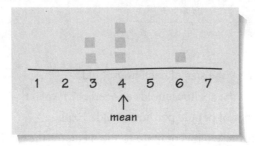

Getting Ready for Problem 3.2

- How many households are there in each situation?
- What is the total number of people in each situation?
- How do these facts relate to the mean in each case?

52 Data About Us

STUDENT PAGE

Notes _____

_____

_____

_____

A. Find two new data sets for six households that each has a mean of 4 people per household. Use cubes to show each data set. Then make line plots from the cubes.

B. Find two different data sets for seven households that each has a mean of 4 people per household. Use cubes to show each set. Then make line plots from the cubes.

C. A group of seven students find they have a mean of 3 people per household. Find a data set that fits this description. Then make a line plot for this data.

D. 1. A group of six students has a mean of $3\frac{1}{2}$ people per household. Find a data set that fits this description. Then make a line plot for this data.

 2. How can the mean be $3\frac{1}{2}$ people when "half" a person does not exist?

 3. How can you predict when the mean number of people per household will not be a whole number?

ACE Homework starts on page 56.

Investigation 3 What Do We Mean by *Mean*? **53**

Notes _____

_____

_____

_____

A group of middle-school students answered the question: How many movies did you watch last month? The table and stem plot show their data.

Movies Watched

Student	Number
Joel	15
Tonya	16
Rachel	5
Swanson	18
Jerome	3
Leah	6
Beth	7
Mickey	6
Bhavana	3
Josh	11

Movies Watched

0	3 3 5 6 6 7
1	1 5 6 8
2	

Key: 1 | 5 means 15 movies

You have found the mean using cubes to represent the data. You may know the following procedure to find the mean: The **mean** of a set of data is the sum of the values divided by the number of values in the set.

Problem 3.3 Using the Mean

A. Use the movie data to find each number.

1. the total number of students

2. the total number of movies watched

3. the mean number of movies watched

B. A new value is added for Carlos, who was home last month with a broken leg. He watched 31 movies.

1. How does the new value change the distribution on the stem plot?

2. Is this new value an outlier? Explain.

3. What is the mean of the data now?

4. Compare the mean from Question A to the new mean. What do you notice? Explain.

Notes _____

_____

_____

_____

C. Data for eight more students are added:

Tommy	5	Robbie	4
Alexandra	5	Ana	4
Trevor	5	Alicia	2
Kirsten	4	Brian	2

1. How do these values change the distribution on the stem plot?

2. Are any of these new data values outliers? Explain.

3. What is the mean of the data now?

4. Compare the means you found in Questions A and B with this new mean. What do you notice? Explain.

D. 1. What happens to the mean of a data set when you add one or more data values that are outliers? Explain.

2. What happens to the mean of a data set when you add data values that cluster near one end of the original data set? Explain.

3. Explain why you think these changes might occur.

ACE Homework starts on page 56.

Notes _____

_____

_____

_____

STUDENT PAGE

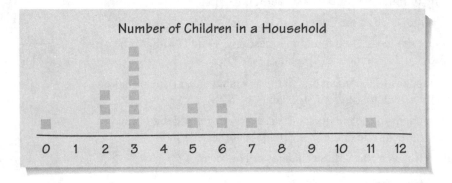

Applications

For Exercises 1 and 2, use the line plot.

Number of Children in a Household

0 1 2 3 4 5 6 7 8 9 10 11 12

1. a. What is the median number of children for the 16 households? Explain how to find the median. What does the median tell you?

   b. Do any of the 16 households have the median number of children? Explain.

2. a. What is the mean number of children per household for the 16 households? Explain how to find the mean. What does the mean tell you?

   b. Do any of the 16 households have the mean number of children? Explain.

For Exercises 3 and 4, the mean number of people per household for eight students is 6 people.

3. Multiple Choice What is the total number of people in the eight households?

   A. 11   **B.** 16   **C.** 48   **D.** 64

4. a. Make a line plot showing one possible arrangement for the numbers of people in the eight households.

   b. Make a line plot showing a different possible arrangement for the numbers of people in the eight households.

   c. Are the medians the same for the two arrangements you made?

Go Online
PHSchool.com
For: Multiple-Choice Skills
Web Code: ama-8354

Notes _____

_____

_____

_____

5. A group of nine students has a mean of $3\frac{1}{3}$ people per household. Make a line plot showing a data set that fits this description.

6. A group of nine students has a mean of 5 people per household. The largest household in the group has 10 people. Make a line plot showing a data set that fits this description.

Connections

7. The students in Mr. Wilson's study hall spent the following amounts of time on their homework.

$\frac{3}{4}$ hour $\frac{1}{2}$ hour $1\frac{1}{4}$ hours $\frac{3}{4}$ hour $\frac{1}{2}$ hour

What is the mean time his students spent on homework?

8. Multiple Choice Use the data from Exercise 7. What is the median time Mr. Wilson's students spent on homework?

F. $\frac{1}{2}$ hour   **G.** $\frac{3}{4}$ hour   **H.** 1 hour   **J.** $1\frac{1}{4}$ hour

9. A soccer league wants to find the average amount of water the players drink per game. There are 18 players on a team and 10 teams in the league. The players drank a total of 5,760 ounces of water during one day in which each team played exactly one game.

   a. How much water did each player drink per game if they each drank the same amount of water?

   b. Does this value represent the mean or the median? Explain.

Investigation 3 What Do We Mean by *Mean*?   **57**

Notes _____

_____

_____

_____

10. A grocery store carries nine different brands of granola bars. What are possible prices for the nine brands if the mean price is $2.66? Explain. You may use pictures to help you.

11. Ralph has a pet rabbit that is 5 years old. He wonders if his rabbit is old compared to other rabbits. He finds out that the mean life span for a rabbit is 7 years.

    a. What does the mean tell Ralph about the life span for a rabbit?

    b. What additional information would help Ralph to predict the life span of his rabbit?

12. Sabrina, Diego, and Marcus entered a dance contest that ran from 9 a.m. to 7 p.m. Below are the times that each student danced.

Homework Help Online
PHSchool.com
For: Help with Exercise 12
Web Code: ame-8312

Dance Contest Schedule

Student	Time
Sabrina	9:15 a.m. to 1:00 p.m.
Diego	1:00 p.m. to 4:45 p.m.
Marcus	4:45 p.m. to 7:00 p.m.

    a. Write the time each student spent dancing as a mixed number.

    b. Look at the data from part (a). Without doing any computations, do you think the mean time spent dancing is the same as, less than, or greater than the median? Explain your reasoning.

For Exercises 13–16, a recent time study of 3,000 children ages 2–18 years old was conducted. The data are in the table below.

How Children Spend Their Time

Activity	Average Time (minutes per day)
Watching videos	39
Reading for fun	44
Using the computer for fun	21

13. Did each child watch videos for 39 minutes per day? Explain.

14. Thelma decides to round 39 minutes to 40 minutes. Then she estimates that children spend about $\frac{2}{3}$ of an hour watching videos. What percent of an hour is $\frac{2}{3}$?

15. Estimate what part of an hour children spend reading for fun. Write your answer as a fraction and as a decimal.

Notes _____

_____

_____

_____

16. Children use a computer for fun for about 20 minutes per day. How many hours do they spend using a computer for fun in 1 week (7 days)? Write your answer as a fraction and as a decimal.

17. Three candidates are running for mayor of Slugville. Each has determined the typical income for the people in Slugville, and they are using this information to help in their campaigns.

Mayor Phillips is running for re-election. He says, "Slugville is doing great! The average income for each person is $2,000 per week!"

Candidate Lily Jackson says, "Slugville is nice, but it needs my help! The average income is only $100 per week."

Candidate Ronnie Ruis says, "Slugville is in a lot of trouble! The average income is $0 per week."

Some of the candidates are confused about "average." Slugville has only 16 residents, and their weekly incomes are $0, $0, $0, $0, $0, $0, $0, $0, $200, $200, $200, $200, $200, $200, $200, and $30,600.

a. Explain which measure of center each of the candidates used as an "average" income for the town. Check their computations.

b. Does any person in Slugville have the mean income? Explain.

c. Does any person in Slugville have an income that equals the median? Explain.

d. Does any person in Slugville have an income that equals the mode? Explain.

e. What do you consider to be the typical income for a resident of Slugville? Explain.

f. Suppose four more people move to Slugville. Each has a weekly income of $200. How would the mean, median, and mode change?

Notes _____

_____

_____

_____

18. A recent survey asked 25 middle-school students how many movies they watch in one month. The data are shown below. Notice that the data vary from 1 movie to 30 movies.

Movies Watched

Student	Number
Wes	2
Tomi	15
Ling	13
Su Chin	1
Michael	9
Mara	30
Alan	20
Jo	1
Tanisha	25
Susan	4
Gil	3
Enrique	2
Lonnie	3
Ken	10
Kristina	15
Mario	12
Henry	5
Julian	2
Alana	4
Tyrone	1
Rebecca	4
Anton	11
Jun	8
Raymond	8
Angelica	17

a. Make a stem-and-leaf plot to show these data. Describe the shape of the data.

b. Find the mean number of movies watched by the students. Explain.

c. What do the mean and the least and greatest values tell you about the typical number of movies watched for this group of students?

d. Find the median number of movies watched. Are the mean and the median the same? Why do you think this is so?

Notes _____

_____

_____

_____

19. Six students each had a different number of pens. They put them all together and then distributed them so that each student had the same number of pens.

    a. Choose any of the following that could be the number of pens they had altogether. Explain your reasoning.

        A. 12   **B.** 18   **C.** 46   **D.** 48

    b. Use your response from part (a). How many pens did each person have after the pens were distributed evenly?

    c. Your classmate says that finding the mean number of pens per person is the same as finding the number of pens each person had after the pens were distributed evenly. Do you agree or disagree? Explain.

Extensions

For Exercises 20 and 21, use the newspaper headline.

20. Do you think that this headline is referring to a mean, a median, or something else? Explain.

21. About how many hours per day does the average third grader watch television if he or she watches 1,170 hours in a year?

Notes _____

_____

_____

_____

22. Review the jump-rope data from Problem 2.2.

   a. What are the median and the mean for each class's data? How do the median and the mean compare for each class?

   b. Should Mr. Costo's class use the median or the mode to compare their performance with Mrs. Reid's class? Why?

   c. What happens to the median of Mr. Costo's class data if you leave out the data for the student who jumped rope 300 times? Why does this happen?

   d. What happens to the mean of Mr. Costo's class data if you leave out the data for the student who jumped rope 300 times? Why does this happen?

   e. Can Mrs. Reid's class claim they did better if Mr. Costo's class leaves out the data of 300 jumps? Explain.

23. A group of middle-school students answered the question: How many TV shows did you watch last week? The table at the right shows their data.

   a. Use the data to find the mean number of TV shows watched.

   b. A new value is added for Albert. He watched only 1 TV show last week.

      i. Is this new value an outlier?

      ii. What is the mean of the data now?

      iii. Compare this mean to the mean you found in part (a). What do you notice? Explain.

Student	Number of TV Shows Watched
Caleb	17
Malek	13
Jenna	20
Mario	8
Melania	11
Bennett	13
Anna	16

62 Data About Us

Notes _____

_____

_____

_____

Mathematical Reflections 3

In this investigation, you have explored a type of measure of center called the mean. It is important to understand this mean, or average, and to relate it to the mode and the median. The following questions will help you summarize what you have learned.

Think about your answers to these questions. Discuss your ideas with other students and your teacher. Then write a summary of your findings in your notebook.

1. Describe a method for calculating mean. Explain why this method works.

2. You have used three measures of center: mode, median, and mean.

   a. Why do you suppose they are called "measures of center"?

   b. What does each tell you about a set of data?

   c. Why might you use the median instead of the mean?

3. You have also used range and how data vary from least to greatest values to describe data. Why might you use these with a measure of center to describe a data set?

4. Once you collect data to answer questions, you must decide what statistics you can use to describe your data.

   a. One student says you can only use the mode to describe categorical data, but you can use the mode, median, and mean to describe numerical data. Is the student correct? Explain.

   b. Can you find range for categorical data? Explain.

Unit Project What's Next?

For your project for the unit, you are developing your own survey to gather information about middle-school students. What statistics can you use to describe the data you might collect for each question in your survey?

Notes _____

_____

_____

Investigation

ACE Assignment Choices

Problem 3.1
Core 1–4
Other *Connections* 7, 8, 19

Problem 3.2
Core 5, 10
Other *Applications* 6; *Extensions* 20, 21;
unassigned choices from previous problems

Problem 3.3
Core 11, 17, 23
Other *Connections* 9, 12–16, 18; *Extensions* 22;
unassigned choices from previous problems

Adapted For suggestions about adapting
Exercise 6 and other ACE exercises, see the
CMP *Special Needs Handbook*.
Connecting to Prior Units 7, 8, 10, 12–16: *Bits and Pieces I*

Applications

1. **a.** 3; order the data from least to greatest. The
   median is the value that separates the data
   in half.

   b. Yes, six households have 3 children. The
   median is located using the data values.
   The only time the median will not be one
   of the data values is when it is determined
   by finding the mean of two middle values
   that are not the same.

2. **a.** 4; you can add the data values together and
   divide by the number of data values to get
   the mean. Or, you can find the mean by
   making stacks of cubes for each of the
   households and then evening out the stacks
   so there are 16 households, each with
   4 members. The mean tells you the value
   that each data item would have if all the
   data had the same value.

b. There are no squares over the number 4 on
the line plot, which means there are no
households in the data set with four
children. This is possible because there are
households with more than four children
and households with less than four children
to balance each other.

3. C

4. **a.** Possible line plot:

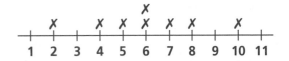

b. Possible line plot:

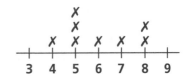

c. Answers will vary.

5. Possible line plot:

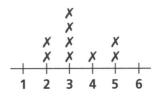

For nine households to have a mean of
$3\frac{1}{3}$ people, there would have to be a total of
$9 \times 3\frac{1}{3}$, or 30 people.

6. Possible answer:

ACE ANSWERS 3

Connections

7. $\frac{3}{4}$ hour. One way students can think of this problem is by using blocks that each represent one fourth, then making towers that correspond to the data values. For example, $\frac{3}{4}$ would be represented by a tower of three blocks, $\frac{1}{2}$ by a tower of two blocks, and so on. By distributing the blocks evenly, students can see that all the towers will have three blocks, which represents a mean of $\frac{3}{4}$.

8. G

9. **a.** 32 oz per player;
   5,760 oz ÷ (18 × 10) players = 32 oz

   b. The mean, because it represents the total amount of water evenly shared among the 180 players.

10. The typical price of a box of granola bars is $2.66, and there are nine different brands of granola. So the total cost of nine boxes (one of each brand) is $23.94. You have to price the boxes so the total cost is $23.94. You could have the nine brands all priced at $2.66, or have just a few priced at $2.66, or have no brands priced at $2.66. Here is one possibility: $2.70, $2.78, $2.98, $2.34, $2.58, $2.70, $2.50, $2.58, $2.78

11. **a.** The mean tells Ralph that if all the rabbits in the data lived to be the same age, that age would be 7 years. What actually happens is that some of the rabbits don't live to 7 years and some of the rabbits live beyond 7 years.

    b. Knowing the spread would give Ralph more information about the possible life span of his rabbit.

12. **a.** Sabrina and Diego danced $3\frac{3}{4}$ hours and Marcus danced $2\frac{1}{4}$ hours.

    b. The mean is less than the median. The median is $3\frac{3}{4}$ hours, and mean is less than $3\frac{3}{4}$ hours because $2\frac{1}{4}$ hours decreases the amount of hours each person danced.

13. No, some children may have watched videos for 39 minutes, but most children spent less or more time watching videos.

14. About 67%

15. About $\frac{3}{4}$ or 0.75 of an hour

16. $2\frac{1}{3}$ hours or about 2.3 hours

17. **a.** Mayor Phillips determined the mean income. The total income is $32,000; dividing by the number of incomes, 16, gives $2,000 per week. Lily Jackson found the median income. There are a total of 16 values, so the median is between the eight and ninth values. The eighth value is $0 and the ninth value is $200, so the median is $100. Ronnie Ruis looked at the mode, which is $0. Each of their computations is correct.

    b. No; no one earns $2,000 per week.

    c. No; no one earns $100 per week.

    d. Yes; eight people earn $0 per week.

    e. $200 is a good answer. Possible explanation: The people who have $0 incomes are probably children, so the people who earn $200 and the person who earns $30,600 are the residents who are employed. The "typical" income is either the median or the mode since the mean is greatly affected by the one large income.

    f. The mode is $200. The median is $200. The mean is $1,640.

18. **a.** Possible answer: The data are skewed to the lower values.

Movies Watched

0	1 1 1 2 2 2 3 3 4 4 4 5 8 8 9
1	0 1 2 3 5 5 7
2	0 5
3	0

Key: 1 | 5 means 15 movies

   b. 9 movies; add to find the total number of the movies watched (225). Then divide the total by the number of students (25).

   c. The mean is 9 movies, and the data vary from 1 to 30 movies. Since the mean is closer to the low end of the data values, more students fall in the low end of the data values.

   d. The median number of movies watched is 8. The mean is greater than the median because the large values pull the mean up, but have less influence on the median.

19. a. A, B, and D because they are divisible by 6.

   b. 2 pens (12 ÷ 6 = 2), 3 pens (18 ÷ 6 = 3), or 8 pens (48 ÷ 6 = 8)

   c. I agree because an average can be found by sharing the total amount of pens evenly among all students.

Extensions

20. Answers will vary. Pay attention to the students' reasoning. Generally, data reported in newspapers use the mean.

21. There are 365 days in a year. This means the average third grader watches 1,170 ÷ 365, or about $3\frac{1}{5}$ hours of television per day.

22. a. Mrs. Reid's class:

   mean: $\approx 38\frac{1}{2}$ (1,157 ÷ 30); median: 28

   Mr. Costo's class:

   mean: $54\frac{2}{5}$ (1,632 ÷ 30); median: 34

   The mean is greater than the median for each class, because there are some greater values in each set of data.

   b. They should use the median, because it is greater than the mode.

   c. The median decreases by 1 to 33 jumps. The median is the middle data value, so it is not changed much by removing the greatest data value.

   d. The mean is now (1,332 ÷ 29) or $45\frac{27}{29}$ or 45.931. The mean decreases by a little more than 8 jumps. It decreases because the greatest value was removed, which had a big influence on the mean.

   e. Mrs. Reid's class's mean and median are still less than each of the same statistics for Mr. Costo's class, so Mrs. Reid's class cannot make a valid claim that they did better.

23. a. 14

   b. i. Yes, 1 is an outlier.

   ii. 12.375

   iii. The new mean is lower. Possible explanation: By adding the 1 to the data, the mean decreases because, like with the cube stacks in Problem 4.1, cubes need to be added to the stack of one, and this would decrease the heights of the other stacks.

Possible Answers to Mathematical Reflections

1. Possible method: Add together all the values. Divide the sum by the number of values. This method works because the sum of the values tells us how much is to be shared or "evened out." The number of values is the number of parts into which the total must be divided. Division gives the number in each part.

2. a. They are measures of center because they are good indicators of a typical value.

   b. The mode is the data value that occurs most frequently. The median is the middle value that separates an ordered set of data in half. The mean is the "balance point," or the value that each item would have if all the data had the same value.

   c. The median is not greatly affected by outliers in the data.

3. The least and greatest values give the upper and lower boundaries of the data set, while the range gives the distance between these two values. A measure of center gives a typical value in the data.

4. a. The student is correct. Finding the mode just involves counting the most frequently occurring data value within a data set, so it can be used with both numerical and categorical data. Finding the mean requires dividing a sum by the number of values, and finding the median requires ordering data values from least to greatest. Both cannot be done with categorical data.

   b. No; finding range depends on being able to identify the least and greatest values. You cannot order categorical data in a logical way.

Answers to Looking Back and Looking Ahead

1. **a.** Because the data are quite spread out, it is difficult to display and see a pattern using a line plot or bar graph. In looking at a stem plot, most of the data are clustered from 58″ to 94″. Three values, 114″, 128″, and 147″, may be considered outliers.

Alligator Lengths

```
 5 | 8
 6 | 1 3 8 9
 7 | 2 2 4 4 6 8
 8 | 2 5 6 6 6 8 9
 9 | 0 0 4 4
10 |
11 | 4
12 | 8
13 |
14 | 7
```
Key: 7 | 2 means 72 inches

b. median length: 85″; mean length: 84.96″ or about 85″; I could use either the mean or the median to describe the typical length of an alligator because the two measures are about the same.

c. range: 89″; data vary from 58″ to 147″

2. **a.** Because the data is quite spread out, it is difficult to display and see a pattern using a line plot or bar graph. In looking at a stem plot, most of the data are clustered from 28 lb to 110 lb. Three values, 197 lb, 366 lb, and 640 lb, may be considered outliers. These values are paired with the three outliers in length (147, 640), (114, 197), and (128, 366).

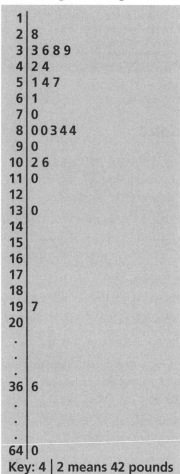

Alligator Weights

```
 1 |
 2 | 8
 3 | 3 6 8 9
 4 | 2 4
 5 | 1 4 7
 6 | 1
 7 | 0
 8 | 0 0 3 4 4
 9 | 0
10 | 2 6
11 | 0
12 |
13 | 0
14 |
15 |
16 |
17 |
18 |
19 | 7
20 |
 . |
 . |
 . |
36 | 6
 . |
 . |
 . |
64 | 0
```
Key: 4 | 2 means 42 pounds

b. median weight: 80 lb; mean weight: about 108.2 lb or 108 lb; I would use the median to describe the typical length of an alligator because the mean is affected by the outliers.

c. range: 612 lb; data vary from 28 lb to 640 lb

3. a. (Figure 1)

   b. i. The numerical value of the weight of the alligators is less than the numerical value of the length.

   ii. The numerical value of weight of the alligators is similar to the numerical value of the length.

   iii. The numerical value of the weight of the alligators is greater than the numerical value of the length. For long alligators, this difference is greater.

   c. i. The numerical value of the weight will be less than the numerical value of the length.

   ii. The numerical value of the weight will be similar to, but probably greater than, the numerical value of the length.

   iii. The numerical value of the weight will be greater than the numerical value of the length.

   d. In Problem 2.3, we learned that arm span and height will be similar regardless of a person's height. The alligator data suggest that, while weight is related to length, the relationship varies based on length. If we know the numerical value of the length, we can estimate the numerical value of the weight as being less than, similar to, or greater than the numerical value of the length. The longer the alligator, the greater the weight.

Note to the Teacher: As the weight of an alligator is directly related to its volume, the relationship between length and volume is cubic.

4. Both mean and median values provide some information about what is "typical" about a data set. When outliers are present, these values may impact the mean more than they impact the median. When the mean and median are similar, the distribution is generally not skewed. However, outliers in the weight do affect the computed mean.

5. The least and greatest values give the lower and upper boundaries of the data. The range gives an idea of how spread out the data are. When the range is small, the data are close together. When the range is greater, the data are more spread out.

6. a. Line plots are used with data that have little spread or variability.

   b. Stem plots help group data that have greater spread or variability so that patterns in the shape of the distribution can be seen.

   c. Coordinate graphs are used with paired data sets when we want to see if changes in one variable are related to changes in another variable.

7. When we say that one variable is related to another variable, it means that one variable appears to depend on another. If we know a person's height, we can estimate his or her arm span. If we know the length of an alligator, we can estimate its weight.

Figure 1

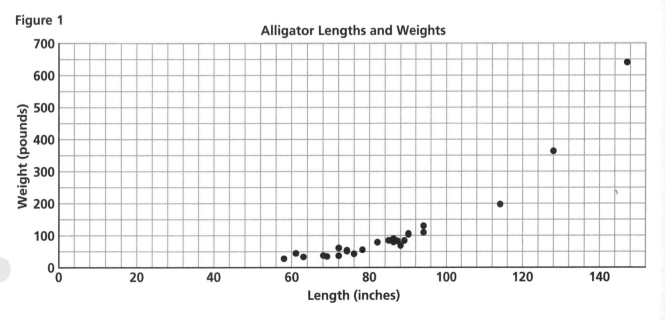

Alligator Lengths and Weights

Guide to the Unit Project

Assigning the Unit Project

The *Is Anyone Typical?* project was introduced at the beginning of the unit and is formally assigned here. Students are asked to use what they have learned in *Data About Us* to conduct a statistical investigation to determine some typical characteristics of middle school students.

Some schools may require administrative approval of surveys; check prior to data collection. It may also be a problem for several classes to conduct surveys independently. You may want to coordinate the data collection among all of the classes so classes from which data are collected are not disturbed several times.

The project can be assigned in a variety of ways. If you have several days available, you can have each group write and conduct a survey consisting of five to ten questions. Each group then collects, analyzes, and interprets the data and prepares a report of their findings. If your time is limited, you may choose to work as a class to develop and conduct the survey. You can then have each group analyze and interpret the data for one question.

A detailed discussion of the project, samples of student projects, and a suggested scoring rubric are given in this section.

Preparing for the Unit Project

This project requires students to conduct a statistical investigation to determine some "typical" characteristics of students in their class or their school. As mentioned in the "Assigning the Unit Project" section, each group can tackle their own complete investigation, or you can write a survey as a class and assign each group the task of analyzing and interpreting the results of one survey question.

When you assign the project, remind students of the question they are trying to answer: "What are some characteristics of a typical middle school student?" Remind students of some of the typical characteristics they have already determined, such as height and name length. Then, have a class discussion about the four steps involved in a statistical investigation.

Step 1: Posing Questions

Before writing their surveys, students must decide what information they want to know. An interesting survey will collect both categorical and numerical information. You will want to check each group's list of questions before allowing them to proceed with their survey. You need to be vigilant about the kinds of questions your students ask. Questions that might embarrass students should not be included. Two questions that may help students to focus are: What will you learn from this question? and How will this question help you learn about the typical middle school student? If you are writing the survey as a class, have students brainstorm about questions they might ask and then work together to narrow down the list.

After students have decided what they want to know, they need to make sure the questions they ask are precise and unambiguous. Have a discussion about the types of questions that work best as "fill in the blanks," such as

How old are you in months? _____

and the types of questions that work best if choices are provided. For example,

What do you do when you are bored? Check the one response that best describes you:

____ watch TV	____ listen to the radio
____ read a book	____ play with a pet
____ complain	____ talk on the phone

If students want to know someone's attitude about something, they can ask how strongly they feel about the question being asked. For example,

Circle only one answer: 1 means strongly disagree, and 5 means strongly agree.

Should students be allowed to wear hats in school?
$$1 \quad 2 \quad 3 \quad 4 \quad 5$$

Step 2: Collecting the Data

Students need to decide whether they will survey their class only or a larger group. The survey will need to be produced, duplicated, and distributed. You may want to coordinate the data collection among all of your classes so classes from which data are collected are not disturbed several times.

Step 3: Analyzing the Data

Once they have collected the data, students need to organize, tally, and display the data. They must decide which displays and which measures of centers are appropriate for each set of data.

Step 4: Interpreting the Results

After the data have been analyzed, students need to interpret the results and write a report or create a poster to display their findings. The report should include the questions asked, information about how the data were collected, appropriate data displays and measures of center, and concluding statements about what is typical about the data.

If you create the survey as a class, and assign one question to each group, you will want to come together again as a class to "pool" the results and assemble the characteristics of a typical student. The photo below shows how one teacher displayed the results of a class investigation.

Grading the Unit Project

Suggested Scoring Rubric

This rubric for scoring the *Is Anyone Typical?* project employs a scale that runs from 0 to 4, with a 4+ for work that goes beyond what has been asked for in some unique way. You may use this rubric as presented here or modify it to fit your district's requirements for evaluating and reporting students' work and understanding.

4+ EXEMPLARY RESPONSE
- Complete, with clear, coherent explanations
- Shows understanding of the mathematical concepts and procedures
- Satisfies all essential conditions of the problem and goes beyond what is asked for in some unique way

4 COMPLETE RESPONSE
- Complete, with clear, coherent explanations
- Shows understanding of the mathematical concepts and procedures
- Satisfies all essential conditions of the problem

3 REASONABLY COMPLETE RESPONSE
- Reasonably complete; may lack detail in explanations
- Shows understanding of most of the mathematical concepts and procedures
- Satisfies most of the essential conditions of the problem

2 PARTIAL RESPONSE
- Gives response; explanation may be unclear or lack detail
- Shows some understanding of some of the mathematical concepts and procedures
- Satisfies some essential conditions of the problem

1 INADEQUATE RESPONSE
- Incomplete; explanation is insufficient or not understandable
- Shows little understanding of the mathematical concepts and procedures
- Fails to address essential conditions of the problem

0 NO ATTEMPT
- Irrelevant response
- Does not attempt a solution
- Does not address conditions of the problem

Samples of Student Projects

The samples that follow are from a class in which each group investigated one question. The first project investigates the states that students have visited. The second looks at the class's favorite radio station.

Sample #1

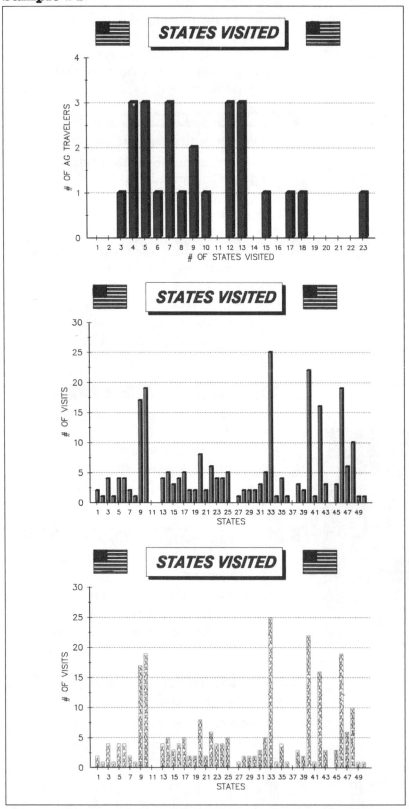

Key

1. Alabama ___
2. Alaska ___
3. Arizona ___
4. Arkansas ___
5. California ___
6. Colorado ___
7. Connecticut ___
8. Deleware ___
9. Flordia ___
10. Georgia ___
11. Hawaii ___
12. Idaho ___
13. Illinois ___
14. Indiana ___
15. Iowa ___
16. Kansas ___
17. Kentucky ___
18. Louisana ___
19. Maine ___
20. Maryland ___
21. Massachusetts
22. Michigan ___
23. Minnesota ___
24. Mississippi ___
25. Missouri ___

26. Montana ___
27. Nebraska ___
28. Nevada ___
29. New hampshire ___
30. New Jersey ___
31. New Mexico ___
32. New York ___
33. North Carolina ___
34. North Dakota ___
35. Ohio ___
36. Oklahoma ___
37. Oregon ___
38. Pennsylvania ___
39. Rhode Island ___
40. South Carolinia
41. South Dakota ___
42. Tennessee ___
43. Texas ___
44. Utah ___
45. Vermont ___
46. Virginia ___
47. Washington ___
48. West Virginia ___
49. Wisconsin ___
50. Wyoming ___

A Teacher's Comments on Sample 1

I evaluated each step of the investigation separately, using a four-point scale for each step. These students received 10 of 16 possible points for their project. I would recommend that they redo the "Interpret the Results" section of their project.

Step 1: Posing Questions (3 points)

These students asked interesting questions. However, they should have clarified what they meant by "been to." Did they mean visited or just traveled through?

Step 2: Collecting the Data (3 points)

The students did not mention the number of students they surveyed. I can determine the number of students that were surveyed from the first graph by counting and adding the heights of the bars $(1 + 3 + 3 + 1 + 3 + 1 + 2 + 1 + 3 + 3 + 1 + 1 + 1 + 1 = 25)$.

Step 3: Analyzing the Data (3 points)

The graphs are quite interesting. Students explored both categorical and numerical data. The first graph shows the numbers of states students have visited. No summary statistics are given for this graph. It is interesting to note that the spread in the number of states visited is from 3 to 25 and the median is between 8 and 9 states.

The other two graphs show categorical data. The first graph is a bar graph. The students used numbers on the horizontal axis to represent the states and provided a key to the right of the graph. The second graph was intended to be a line plot, but has a vertical axis like a bar graph. This vertical axis is not necessary, since the numbers of X's indicate the frequencies. The students determined that the mode state is 40, South Carolina. (These students live in North Carolina, and so did not consider it a "state visited."). These students, correctly, did not include any other statistics for these two graphs. The mean and median are not appropriate measures for categorical data.

Step 4: Interpreting the Results (1 point)

The students provided only one summary statement about their results—that the mode state is South Carolina. They could have discussed the fact that the mode state and the states close to the mode (Virginia, Georgia, Florida, and Tennessee) are neighboring states of North Carolina. They might also have mentioned that, in the first graphs, values of 23, 15, 17, and 18 are unusual values, and explored why these students had visited so many states.

Sample #2

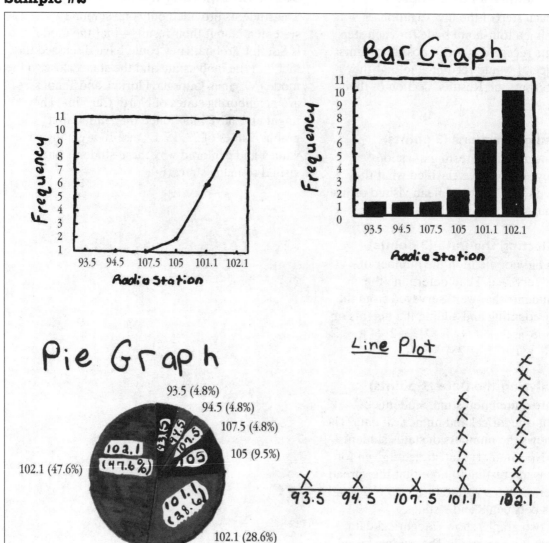

Bar Graph

Pie Graph

Line Plot

Pie Graph labels:
93.5 (4.8%)
94.5 (4.8%)
107.5 (4.8%)
105 (9.5%)
102.1 (47.6%)
101.1 (28.6%)

Bonnie and I have done a math project.
Our question is what is your favorite radio
station? The mode was 102 jams. We didn't have
a mean, median, or range because we're dealing
with station names. Above we have a pie graph,
bar graph, and two types of line plots. They may
look different, but they show the same kind of
data.
Ten people said they liked 102 jams. Six people
said they liked country 101.1. One person said
he liked 107.5, one said he liked 94.5, and
one said he liked 93.5. We had a total of
twenty-one students. That is our project.

A Teacher's Comments on Sample 2

I evaluated each step of the investigation separately, using a four-point scale for each step. These students received 14 of 16 possible points for their project.

Step 1: Posing Questions (4 points)

The question was clearly stated.

Step 2: Collecting the Data (4 points)

The students' summary and three of their four graphs agree that they surveyed 21 students.

Step 3: Analyzing the Data (3 points)

These students used four different displays. The line plot, the bar graph, and the circle graph are appropriate. The line graph is not appropriate because it is designed to show change over time. On the line plot, the X's are not aligned, so the stack of X's for 102.1 looks shorter than it should relative to the stack for 101.1. Also on the line plot, data is missing for 105.

Step 4: Interpreting the Results (3 points)

These students included a summary statement. They acknowledge the inappropriateness of the mean, median, or range for categorical data. I would have liked them to talk a bit more about the radio stations. Stations 101.1 and 102.1 are far more popular than the other four choices.

Unit Project

Is Anyone Typical?

You can use what you have learned in *Data About Us* to conduct a statistical investigation. Answer the question, "What are some characteristics of a typical middle-school student?" Complete your data collection, analysis, and interpretation. Then make a poster, write a report, or find some other way to display your results.

Your statistical investigation should consist of four parts:

- Asking Questions

  Decide what information you want to gather. You will want to gather both numerical data and categorical data. Your data may include physical characteristics, family characteristics, behaviors (such as hobbies), and preferences or opinions.

  Once you have decided what you want to know, write clear and appropriate questions. Everyone who takes your survey should interpret your questions the same way. For some questions, you may want to give answer choices. For example, instead of asking, "What is your favorite movie?" you could ask, "Which of the following movies do you like best?" and list several choices.

- Collecting the Data

  You can collect data from just your class or from a larger group of students. Decide how to distribute and collect the survey.

- Analyzing the Data

  Once you have collected your data, organize, display, and analyze them. Think about what types of displays and which measures of center are most appropriate for each set of data values you collect.

- Interpreting the Results

  Use the results of your analysis to describe some characteristics of the typical middle-school student. Is there a student that fits all the "typical" characteristics you found? If not, explain why.

Notes _____

_____

_____

_____

Looking Back and Looking Ahead

For: Vocabulary Review Puzzle
Web Code: amj-8051

Working on the problems in this unit, you explored some of the big ideas involved in conducting statistical investigations. You learned how to

- use a process of statistical investigation to pose questions, collect and analyze data, and interpret results
- represent data using bar graphs, line plots, stem-and-leaf plots, and coordinate graphs
- explore ways of using statistics such as mean, median, mode, and range to describe what is "typical" about data
- develop a variety of ways to compare data sets

Use Your Understanding: Statistical Reasoning

Naturalists in their studies of wild animal populations often use statistical reasoning. The data in the table on the next page show the lengths (in inches) and weights (in pounds) of 25 alligators captured in central Florida.

Looking Back and Looking Ahead **65**

Notes _____

_____

_____

_____

Lengths and Weights of Captured Alligators

Gator Number	Length (inches)	Weight (pounds)	Gator Number	Length (inches)	Weight (pounds)
1	74	54	14	88	70
2	94	110	15	58	28
3	85	84	16	90	102
4	61	44	17	94	130
5	128	366	18	68	39
6	72	61	19	78	57
7	89	84	20	86	80
8	90	106	21	72	38
9	63	33	22	74	51
10	82	80	23	147	640
11	114	197	24	76	42
12	69	36	25	86	90
13	86	83			

1. Consider the lengths of the alligators in the sample.

  a. Make a graph of the lengths of the 25 alligators. Describe the distribution of lengths in the graph.

  b. What are the mean and median lengths? Which might you use to describe the typical length of an alligator?

  c. What are the range and the least and greatest values of the lengths?

2. Consider the weights of alligators in the sample.

  a. Make a graph of the weights of the 25 alligators. Describe the distribution of weights in the graph.

  b. What are the mean and median weights? Which might you use to describe the typical weight of an alligator?

  c. What are the range and the least and greatest values of the weights?

Notes _____

_____

_____

_____

3. a. Make a coordinate graph of the (*length*, *weight*) data.

   b. What do you notice about the relationship between length and weight of alligators in the sample that are

   i. 61 and 63 inches long?   **ii.** 82, 85, and 86 inches long?

   iii. 90, 94, and 114 inches long?

   c. What weight would you predict for an alligator that is

   i. 70 inches long?   **ii.** 100 inches long?

   iii. 130 inches long?

   d. Do you believe it is possible to make a good estimate for the weight of an alligator if you know its length?

Explain Your Reasoning

When you describe a collection of data, you look for the shape of the distribution of the data. You can often visualize data patterns using graphs.

4. How do the mean and the median help in describing the distribution of data in a data set?

5. How do the range and the least and greatest values help in describing the distribution of data in a data set?

6. How do you know when to use each graph to display numerical data?

   a. line plots   **b.** stem-and-leaf plots   **c.** coordinate graphs

7. What does it mean to say that a person's arm span *is related to* his or her height, or that the weight of an alligator *is related to* its length?

Look Ahead

The ideas about statistics and data analysis that you have learned in this unit will be used and extended in a variety of future *Connected Mathematics* units. In *Data Distributions*, you will explore how data vary and ways to compare data sets. In *Samples and Populations*, you will explore sampling, comparing samples, and comparing different variables in a sample. You'll also find that various statistical plots and data summaries appear in everyday news reports and in the technical work of science, business, and government.

Notes

B

bar graph (bar chart) A graphical representation of a table of data in which the height or length of each bar indicates its frequency. The bars are separated from each other to highlight that the data are discrete or "counted" data. In a vertical bar graph, the horizontal axis shows the values or categories, and the vertical axis shows the frequency or tally for each of the values or categories on the horizontal axis. In a horizontal bar graph, the vertical axis shows the values or categories, and the horizontal axis shows the frequencies.

gráfica de barras (tabla de barras) Representación gráfica de una tabla de datos en la que la altura o longitud de cada barra indica su frecuencia. Las barras están separadas entre sí para subrayar que los datos son discretos o "contados". En una gráfica de barras vertical, el eje horizontal representa los valores o categorías, y el eje vertical representa la frecuencia o el cómputo de cada uno de los valores o categorías en el eje horizontal. En una gráfica de barras horizontal, el eje vertical representa los valores o categorías, y el eje horizontal representa las frecuencias.

Vertical Bar Graph

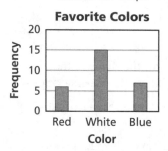

Horizontal Bar Graph

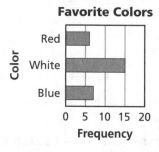

C

categorical data Data that are "words" that represent possible responses within a given category. Frequency counts can be made of the entries for a given category. The table below shows examples of categories and their possible entries.

datos categóricos Valores que son "palabras" que representan respuestas posibles en una categoría dada. Se pueden contar las frecuencias de las entradas para una categoría dada. La siguiente tabla muestra ejemplos de categorías y sus posibles entradas.

Category	Possible Entries
Month people are born	January, February, March
Favorite color to wear	magenta, blue, yellow
Kinds of pets people have	cats, dogs, fish, horses

Notes _____

_____

_____

_____

coordinate graph A graphical representation in which points are used to denote pairs of related numerical values. For each point, the two coordinates of the point give the associated numerical values in the appropriate order. Using the table below, the x-coordinate could represent height, and the y-coordinate could represent arm span. The coordinate graph would look like the one below the table.

gráfica de coordenadas Representación gráfica en la que se usan puntos para denotar los pares de valores numéricos relacionados. Para cada punto, las dos coordenadas del punto dan los valores numéricos asociados en el orden apropiado. En la tabla de abajo, la coordenada x podría representar la altura y la coordenada y podría representar la longitud del brazo. La gráfica de coordenada sería como la que está debajo de la tabla.

Height and Arm Span Measurements

Initials	Height (inches)	Arm Span (inches)
JJ	69	67
NY	63	60
CM	73	75
PL	77	77

Height and Arm Span Measurements

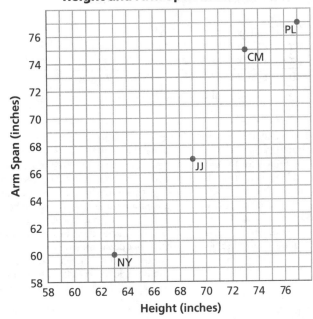

English/Spanish Glossary   **69**

Notes _____

_____

_____

D

data Values such as counts, ratings, measurements, or opinions that are gathered to answer questions. The data in this table show mean temperatures in three cities.

datos Valores como cómputos, calificaciones, medidas u opiniones que se recogen para responder a preguntas. Los datos en esta tabla representan las temperaturas medias en tres ciudades.

Daily Mean Temperatures

City	Mean Temperature (°F)
Mobile, Ala.	67.5
Boston, Mass.	51.3
Spokane, Wash.	47.3

L

line plot A quick, simple way to organize data along a number line where the Xs (or other symbols) above a number represent how often each value is mentioned.

diagrama de puntos Una manera rápida y sencilla de organizar datos en una recta numérica donde las X (u otros símbolos) colocadas encima de un número representan la frecuencia con que se menciona cada valor.

Number of Siblings Students Have

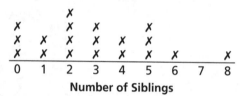

Number of Siblings

M

mean The value you would get if all the data are combined and then redistributed evenly. For example, the total number of siblings for the above data is 56 siblings. If all 19 students had the same number of siblings, they would each have about 3 siblings. Differences from the mean "balance out" so that the sum of differences below and above the mean equal 0. The mean of a set of data is the sum of the values divided by the number of values in the set.

media El valor se logra que si todos los datos se combinan y después se redistribuyen uniformemente. Por ejemplo, el número total de hermanos y hermanas para los datos en el diagrama de arriba es de 56. Si los 19 estudiantes tuvieran la misma cantidad de hermanos y hermanas, cada uno tendría aproximadamente 3 hermanos o hermanas. Las diferencias de la media se "equilibran" de tal manera que la suma de las diferencias por encima y por debajo de la media es igual a 0. La media de un conjunto de datos es la suma de los valores dividido por el número de valores en el conjunto.

median The number that marks the middle of an ordered set of data. At least half of the values lie at or above the median, and at least half lie at or below the median. The median of the distribution of siblings is 3 because the tenth (middle) value in the ordered set of 19 values (0, 0, 0, 1, 1, 2, 2, 2, 2, 3, 3, 3, 4, 4, 5, 5, 5, 6, 8) is 3 siblings.

mediana El número que señala la mitad en un conjunto ordenado de datos. Por lo menos mitad de los datos ocurre en o encima de la mediana, y por lo menos mitad de los datos ocurre en o debajo de la mediana. La mediana de la distribución de hermanos y hermanas es 3 porque el décimo valor (el del medio) en el conjunto ordenado de 19 valores (0, 0, 0, 1, 1, 2, 2, 2, 2, 3, 3, 3, 4, 4, 5, 5, 5, 6, 8) es 3 hermanos o hermanas.

70 Data About Us

Notes

mode The category or numerical value that occurs most often. The mode of the distribution of siblings is 2. It is possible for a set of data to have more than one mode.

moda En una distribución, es la categoría o el valor numérico que ocurre con mayor frecuencia. La moda de la distribución de hermanos o hermanas es 2. Es posible que un conjunto de datos tenga más de una moda.

N

numerical data Values that are numbers such as counts, measurements, and ratings. Here are some examples.
- Number of children in families
- Pulse rates (number of heart beats per minute)
- Height
- Amount of time people spend reading in one day
- Amount of value placed on something, such as: on a scale of 1 to 5 with 1 as "low interest," how would you rate your interest in participating in the school's field day?

datos numéricos Valores que son números como, por ejemplo, cómputos, medidas y calificaciones. Aquí hay algunos ejemplos.
- Número de hijos e hijas en las familias
- Pulsaciones por minuto (número de latidos del corazón por minuto)
- Altura
- Cantidad de tiempo que las personas pasan leyendo en un día
- El valor que las personas le dan a algo, como por ejemplo: en una escala de 1 a 5, en la que 1 representa "poco interés", ¿cómo calificarías tu interés por participar en el día de campo de tu escuela?

O

outlier A value that lies far from the "center" of a distribution. Outlier is a relative term, but it indicates a data point that is much higher or much lower than the values that could be normally expected for the distribution.

valor extremo Valor que se sitúa lejos del "centro" de una distribución. El valor extremo es un término relativo, pero indica un dato que es mucho más alto o mucho más bajo que los valores que se podrían esperar normalmente de la distribución.

R

range The difference between the least value and the greatest value in a distribution. For example, in the distribution below, the range of the number of siblings is 8 people.

gama Diferencia entre el valor mínimo y máximo en una distribución. Por ejemplo, en la siguiente distribución, la gama del número de hermanos o hermanas es 8 personas.

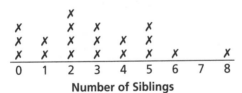

Number of Siblings Students Have

Number of Siblings

S

scale The size of the units on an axis of a graph or number line. For instance, each mark on the vertical axis might represent 10 units.

escala El tamaño de las unidades en un eje de una gráfica o recta numérica. Por ejemplo, cada marca en el eje vertical puede representar 10 unidades.

English/Spanish Glossary **71**

Notes

stem-and-leaf plot (stem plot) A quick way to picture the shape of a distribution while including the actual numerical values in the graph. For a number like 25, the stem 2 is written at the left of the vertical line, and the leaf, 5 is at the right.

diagrama de tallo y hojas Una manera rápida de representar la forma de una distribución y al mismo tiempo incluir los valores numéricos reales en la gráfica. Para un número como 25, el tallo 2 se escribe a la izquierda de la recta vertical, y la hoja 5, a la derecha de la recta.

Travel Time

0	
1	5 5 5 5
2	2 5 0
3	0 5
4	
5	
6	0

Key: 2 | 5 means 25 min.

survey A method for collecting data that uses interviews. Surveys ask questions to find out information such as facts, opinions, or beliefs.

encuesta Un método para reunir datos que utiliza entrevistas. En las encuestas se hacen preguntas para averiguar información tal como hechos, opiniones o creencias.

T

table A tool for organizing information in rows and columns. Tables let you list categories or values and then tally the occurrences.

tabla Una herramienta para organizar información en filas y columnas. Las tablas permiten que se hagan listas de categorías o de valores y luego se computan los sucesos.

Favorite Colors

Color	Number of Students
Red	6
White	15
Blue	9

X

x-axis The horizontal number line used to make a graph.

eje x Recta numérica horizontal que se usa para hacer una gráfica.

Y

y-axis The vertical number line used to make a graph.

eje y Recta numérica vertical que se usa para hacer una gráfica.

72 Data About Us

Notes

Academic Vocabulary

The following terms are important to your understanding of the mathematics in this unit. Knowing and using these words will help you in thinking, reasoning, representing, communicating your ideas, and making connections across ideas. When these words make sense to you, the investigations and problems will make more sense as well.

analyze To study using a logical or mathematical system.

related terms: examine, evaluate, determine, observe, investigate

Sample: Analyze the following data to find the mean and the mode.

Getting to School

Student	Krista	Mike	Lupe	Kareem
Time (min)	10	15	20	10

The mean is $\frac{10 + 15 + 20 + 10}{4} = 13.75$.
The mode of this data is 10 because 10 is the value that occurs most often.

analizar Estudiar usando un sistema lógico o matemático.

términos relacionados: examinar, evaluar, determinar, observar, investigar

Ejemplo: Analiza los siguientes datos para hallar la media y la moda.

Tiempos a la escuela

Estudiante	Krista	Mike	Lupe	Kareem
Tiempo (minutos)	10	15	20	10

La media es $\frac{10 + 15 + 20 + 10}{4} = 13.75$.
La moda de estos datos es 10 porque 10 es el valor que ocurre con mayor frecuencia.

explain To give facts and details that make an idea easier to understand. Explaining can involve a written summary supported by a diagram, chart, table, or a combination of these.

related terms: analyze, clarify, describe, justify, tell

Sample: Explain why the mean may not be the best statistical measure of how many sit-ups students can do.

How many sit-ups?

```
0 | 9 9
1 | 0 1 2 2 5 5 6
2 |
3 |
4 | 1
Key 1 | 2 = 12
```

The mean is affected by the outlier 41, which is much greater than the rest of the data. The median or mode would be better measures of the data.

explicar Dar hechos y detalles que hacen que una idea sea más fácil de comprender. Explicar puede implicar un resumen escrito apoyado por hechos, un diagrama, una gráfica, una tabla o una combinación de éstos.

términos relacionados: analizar, aclarar, describir, justificar, decir

Ejemplo: Explica por qué la media puede no ser la mejor medida estadística de cuántas sentadillas pueden hacer los estudiantes.

¿Cuántas sentadillas?

```
0 | 9 9
1 | 0 1 2 2 5 5 6
2 |
3 |
4 | 1
Clave 1 | 2 = 12
```

La media se ve afectada por el valor extremo 41, que es mucho más grandes que el resto de los datos. La mediana o la moda serían mejores medidas de los datos.

Academic Vocabulary **73**

Notes _____

_____

_____

_____

P

predict To make an educated guess based on the analysis of real data.

related terms: estimate, guess, expect

Sample: **Dan knows that the mean life span of his type of tropical fish is 2 years. What other information could help Dan predict how long his fish will live?**

> If Dan also knew the median life span he would have more information to predict how long his fish will live. The mean could be skewed because of one or more outliers.

predecir Hacer una conjetura informada basada en el análisis de datos reales.

términos relacionados: estimar, conjeturar, esperar

Ejemplo: **Dan sabe que la duración de la vida media de su tipo de pez tropical es de 2 años. ¿Qué otra información podría ayudar a Dan a predecir cuánto vivirá su pez?**

> Si Dan también supiera la duración de la vida media, tendría más información para predecir cuánto vivirá su pez. La media podría estar sesgada debido a uno o más valores extremos.

R

represent To stand for or take the place of something else. Symbols, equations, charts, and tables are often used to represent particular situations.

related terms: symbolize, stand for

Sample: **Jerry surveyed his classmates about the number of pets they have. He recorded his data in a table. Represent the results of Jerry's survey in a bar graph.**

representar Significar o tomar el lugar de algo más. Con frecuencia se usan símbolos, ecuaciones, gráficas y tablas para representar situaciones particulares.

términos relacionados: simbolizar, significar

Ejemplo: **Jerry hizo una encuesta entre sus compañeros de clases sobre el número de mascotas que tienen. Anotó sus datos en una tabla. Representa los resultados de la encuesta de Jerry en una gráfica de barras.**

How Many Pets?

Number of Pets	Number of Students
0 pets	10
1 pet	11
2 or more pets	8

¿Cuántas mascotas?

Número de mascotas	Número de estudiantes
0 mascotas	10
1 mascota	11
2 ó más mascotas	8

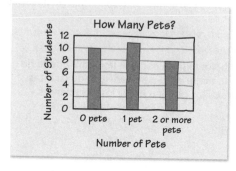

74 Data About Us

Notes _____

_____

_____

_____

Index

Acting it out, 11–12, 50–51, 53

Algebra
  axis 39, 40, 47
  compute 4, 58, 59
  coordinate graph 4, 30, 37–39, 40, 42, 47, 48, 65, 67
  data 4, 7, 8–23, 25, 28, 29, 30, 32–43, 46–49, 51, 54, 55, 57–65, 67
  data set 9, 12, 13, 29, 35, 51, 53–55, 57, 63–65
  graph 11, 17, 22–25, 37–41, 46–48, 66, 67
  horizontal axis 18, 24, 28, 40
  line 38, 47
  numerical data 4, 14, 17, 23, 25, 29, 49, 63, 64
  plot 37, 40
  point 37–39, 47, 48
  variable 67
  x-axis 37, 42
  y-axis 37, 42

Average (*also see* Mean), 4, 49–50, 57, 59, 63

Axis (axes), coordinate, 37, 69
  horizontal, 37, 40
  vertical, 37, 40
  x-axis, 37, 42, 69, 74
  y-axis, 37, 42, 69, 74

Back-to-back stem plot, 43, 44, 48

Bar graph, 8–9, 16–20, 29, 43, 48, 68
  ACE, 21–22, 24–25, 26–28
  making, 9, 20, 21–22, 28, 43
  horizontal, 18–20, 68
  vertical, 18–20, 26, 68
  double, 27
  stacked, 27

Books
  Chuks-orji, Ogonna, 13
  Do People Grow on Family Trees?, 13
  Names from Africa, 13
  Wolfman, Ira, 13

Categorical data, 4, 14, 17, 23, 25, 29, 63, 68

Census, 3, 49–50

Chuks-orji, Ogonna, 13

Collecting data (*also see* Data, collecting), 5, 9, 29, 38, 48, 53, 63, 64

Coordinate axes, 37, 40, 42, 69, 74

Coordinate graph, 37–42, 48, 66–67, 69, 73
  ACE, 46–47
  locating points on, 37–38, 48
  making, 38–39, 40, 47, 66
  scale and, 39, 40, 42, 47, 48, 73

Cubes, using, 50–51, 53

Data
  analyzing (*also see* interpreting), 3, 4, 8–20, 49–53, 54–62, 63, 64, 65–66
  categorical, 4, 14, 17, 23, 25, 29, 63, 68
  collecting, 3, 4, 5, 7, 9, 15, 28, 29, 30–31, 34, 36, 38, 46, 48, 53, 60, 63, 64
  distribution, 4, 8–10, 16, 18–20, 21–22, 29, 52, 55, 67
  grouping, 30–39, 40–47, 48
  interpreting, 4, 8–20, 21–28, 29, 38–39
  numerical, 4, 14, 17, 23, 25, 29, 48, 49, 63, 67, 72
  organizing, 4, 6–8, 14–17, 30–38
  outliers and, 35, 54–55, 62, 72
  patterns in, 8, 30, 37–39, 41–42, 47, 66–67
  prediction with, 7, 38, 42, 67
  types of, *see* categorical *and* numerical

Distribution of data, 4, 8–10, 16, 18–20, 29, 52, 55, 67
  ACE, 21–22

Do People Grow on Family Trees?, 13

Double bar graph, 27

Estimation, 25, 28, 58, 67

Family names, 6, 13

Frequency 16, 18, 27

Graph (*also see* Plots)
  bar, 8–9, 16–20, 21–22, 24–25, 26–28, 29, 43, 48, 68
  coordinate, 37–42, 46–48, 66–67, 69, 73
  double bar, 27
  stacked bar, 27

Horizontal axis, 37, 40

Horizontal bar graph, 18–20, 68

Household, 49–53, 56–57

Interpreting data
  back-to-back stem plot, 34, 44, 48
  bar graph, 8–9, 16–20, 21–22, 24–25, 26–28, 29, 43, 48, 68
  coordinate graph, 37–42, 46–47, 48, 66–67, 69, 73
  line plot, 8–11, 21, 29–30, 43, 48, 52–53, 56–57, 67, 70, 72
  picture, 12, 32, 36, 50, 58
  pie chart, 44
  stem-and-leaf plot, 30–35, 40, 43–44, 48, 54–55, 60, 62, 67, 73
  table, 10, 12, 16–17, 29, 31, 36–37, 51, 54–55, 66, 68–70, 74

Investigations, 6–20, 30–39, 49–55

Justify or explain answer, 16–17, 20, 29, 33, 39, 54–55, 63, 67
  ACE, 22, 24–25, 27–28, 40–44, 47, 56–58, 59–62

Justify or explain method, 7, 30, 48, 63, 67
  ACE, 25, 28, 42–43, 47, 62

Line 38, 47

Line plot, 8–11, 29–30, 48, 52–53, 67, 70, 72
  ACE, 21, 43, 56–57
  making, 9, 11, 21, 43, 53, 56–57
  mean and, 52–53, 56–57

Index **75**

Notes
_____
_____
_____
_____

Looking Back and Looking
 Ahead: Unit Reflections,
 65–67

Manipulatives
 cube stacks, 50–51, 53
 grid paper, 11
 index cards, 12

Mathematical Highlights, 4

Mathematical Reflections, 29, 48,
 63

Mean, 4, 49–55, 63, 65–67, 71
 ACE, 56–62
 finding, 49–51, 71
 line plot and, 52–53, 56–57
 outliers and, 55, 62
 prediction with, 58
 stem-and-leaf plot and, 54–55,
 60

Measures of center (*also see*
 Average; Mean; Median;
 Mode), 12, 49, 63, 64

Median, 4, 9, 11–13, 17, 20, 29, 33,
 48, 50, 63, 65–67, 71
 ACE, 21–22, 25, 40, 42, 47,
 56–62
 finding, 9, 71

Mode, 4, 9–12, 17, 29, 50, 63, 65, 71
 ACE, 21–22, 59, 62
 finding, 9, 71

Model
 cube stacks, 50–51, 53
 grid paper, 11
 picture, 12, 32, 36, 50

Names, 5, 6–13
 ACE, 21–22, 26–27
 family, 6, 13
 from Africa, 9, 13
 from China, 13
 from Europe, 13

from Vietnam, 13
 length, 6–7
 meanings, 9, 13
 origins, 6, 13

Name meanings, 9, 13

Name origins, 6, 13

Names from Africa, 13

Notebook, 29, 48, 63

Numerical data, 4, 14, 17, 23, 25,
 29, 48, 49, 63, 67, 72

Outliers, 35, 54–55, 62, 72
 mean and, 55, 62

Patterns, in data, 8, 30, 37–39,
 41–42, 47, 66–67

Picture, 12, 32, 36, 50, 58

Pie chart, 44

Plot
 line, 8–11, 21, 29–30, 43, 48,
 52–53, 56–57, 67, 70, 72
 stem-and-leaf, 30–35, 40,
 43–44, 48, 54–55, 60, 62, 67,
 73

Point 37–39, 47, 48

Problem-solving strategies
 acting it out, 11–12, 50–51, 53
 collecting data, 5, 9, 29, 38, 48,
 53, 63, 64
 looking for a pattern, 8, 30,
 37–39, 41–42, 47, 66–67
 making a bar graph, 9, 20,
 21–22, 28, 43
 making a coordinate graph,
 38–39, 40, 47, 66
 making a line plot, 9, 11, 21, 43,
 53, 56–57
 making a stem-and-leaf plot,
 32–33, 40, 43–44, 48, 60
 making a table, 21, 21, 43
 using cubes, 50–51, 53

Prediction
 using data, 7, 38, 42, 67
 using mean, 58
 using range, 25

Range, 4, 9–11, 17, 29, 33, 48, 63,
 65–67, 72
 ACE, 21–22, 25, 47
 finding, 9, 72
 prediction with, 25

Scale, and coordinate graphs, 39,
 40, 42, 47, 48, 73

Set 39, 54

Stacked bar graph, 27

Statistic 4, 9, 35, 63–65

Statistical investigation, 5, 64

Stem-and-leaf plot, 30–35, 48,
 54–55, 67, 73
 ACE, 40, 43–44, 60, 62
 making, 32–33, 40, 43–44, 48, 60
 back-to-back, 34, 44, 48
 mean and, 54–55, 60

Survey, 3, 73

Table, 10, 12, 16–17, 29, 31, 36–37,
 51, 54–55, 66, 68–70, 74
 ACE, 21, 26, 41, 43, 45–46, 58
 making, 12, 21, 43

Unit project, 5, 29, 48, 63, 64

Variable 67

Vertical axis, 37, 40

Vertical bar graph, 18–20, 26, 68

Wolfman, Ira, 13

x-axis, 37, 42, 69, 74

y-axis, 37, 42, 69, 74

76 Data About Us

Notes _____

_____

_____

_____

Acknowledgments

Team Credits

The people who made up the **Connected Mathematics 2** team—representing editorial, editorial services, design services, and production services— are listed below. Bold type denotes core team members.

Leora Adler, Judith Buice, Kerry Cashman, Patrick Culleton, Sheila DeFazio, Richard Heater, **Barbara Hollingdale, Jayne Holman,** Karen Holtzman, **Etta Jacobs,** Christine Lee, Carolyn Lock, Catherine Maglio, **Dotti Marshall,** Rich McMahon, Eve Melnechuk, Kristin Mingrone, Terri Mitchell, **Marsha Novak,** Irene Rubin, Donna Russo, Robin Samper, Siri Schwartzman, **Nancy Smith,** Emily Soltanoff, **Mark Tricca,** Paula Vergith, Roberta Warshaw, Helen Young

Additional Credits

Diana Bonfilio, Mairead Reddin, Michael Torocsik, nSight, Inc.

Illustration

Michelle Barbera: 7, 20, 30, 59, 60

Technical Illustration

WestWords, Inc.

Cover Design

tom white.images

Photos

2 t, Chris Pinchbeck/IPN; **2 m,** Kwame Zikomo/SuperStock; **2 b,** Michael Newman/PhotoEdit; **3,** Jeff Greenberg/Peter Arnold, Inc.; **6,** Kwame Zikomo/SuperStock; **9,** Ariadne Van Zandbergen/Lonely Planet Images; **13,** Steve Vidler/SuperStock; **15 l,** Rick Gomez/Corbis; **15 r,** Myrleen Ferguson Cate/PhotoEdit; **18,** Ron Kimball/Ron Kimball Stock; **20,** Chris Pinchbeck/IPN; **23,** Ellen Senisi/The Image Works; **33,** Ray Stott/The Image Works; **35,** Kwame Zikomo/SuperStock; **36,** Richard Haynes; **38,** David Young-Wolff/PhotoEdit; **41,** Ellen Senisi/The Image Works; 43, Richard Haynes; **44,** Journal-Courier/Steve Warmowski/The Image Works; **47,** Jim Cummins/Getty Images, Inc.; **49,** Ron Stroud/Masterfile; **53,** Creatas/PictureQuest; **55,** Michael Newman/PhotoEdit; **57,** Bob Daemmrich Photography; **62,** Syracuse Newspapers/The Image Works; **65,** Joe McDonald/Corbis

Note: Every effort has been made to locate the copyright owner of the material reprinted in this book. Omissions brought to our attention will be corrected in subsequent editions.

Acknowledgments **77**

Notes _____

Labsheet 2.4

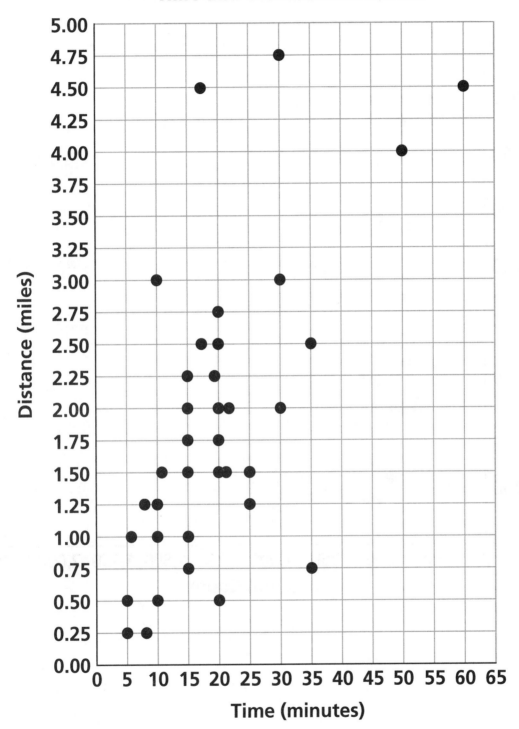

Time and Distances to School

Labsheet 2ACE Exercise 15

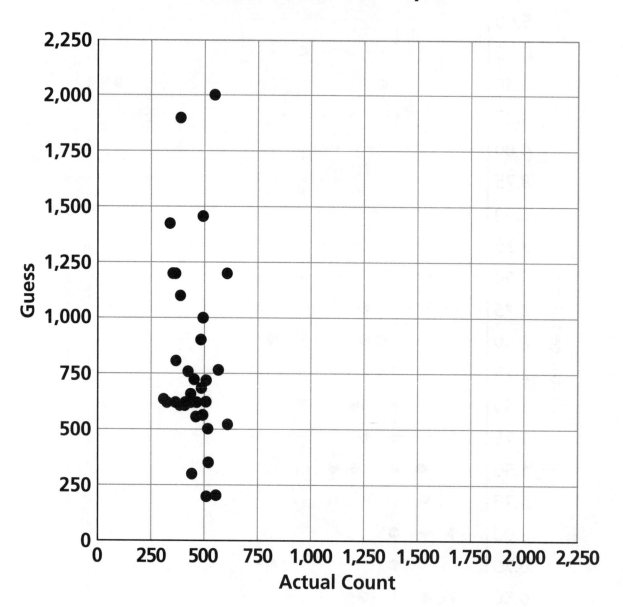

Number of Seeds in Pumpkins

Centimeter Grid Paper

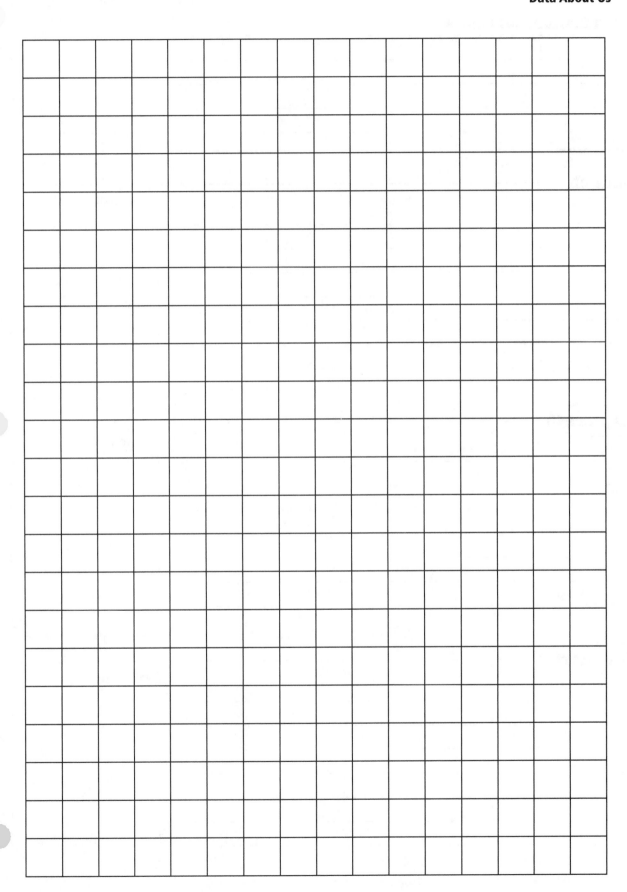

PACING: _____

Mathematical Goals

_____
_____
_____
_____

Launch

_____
_____
_____
_____
_____
_____
_____

Materials

Explore

_____
_____
_____
_____
_____
_____
_____

Materials

Summarize

_____
_____
_____
_____
_____
_____
_____

Materials

B

bar graph (bar chart) A graphical representation of a table of data in which the height or length of each bar indicates its frequency. The bars are separated from each other to highlight that the data are discrete or "counted" data. In a vertical bar graph, the horizontal axis shows the values or categories, and the vertical axis shows the frequency or tally for each of the values or categories on the horizontal axis. In a horizontal bar graph, the vertical axis shows the values or categories, and the horizontal axis shows the frequencies.

Vertical Bar Graph

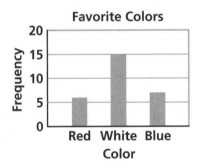

Horizontal Bar Graph

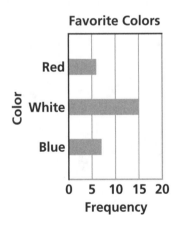

C

categorical data Data that are "words" that represent possible responses within a given category. Frequency counts can be made of the values for a given category. The table below shows examples of categories and their possible values.

Category	Possible Values
Month people are born	January, February, March
Favorite color to wear	magenta, blue, yellow
Kinds of pets people have	cats, dogs, fish, horses

GLOSSARY

coordinate graph A graphical representation in which points are used to denote pairs of related numerical values. For each point, the two coordinates of the point give the associated numerical values in the appropriate order. Using the table below, the x-coordinate could represent height, and the y-coordinate could represent arm span. The coordinate graph would look like the one in Figure 1.

Height and Arm Span Measurements

Initials	Height (inches)	Arm Span (inches)
JJ	69	67
NY	63	60
CM	73	75
PL	77	77

data Values such as counts, ratings, measurements, or opinions that are gathered to answer questions. The data in this table show mean temperatures in three cities.

Daily Mean Temperatures

City	Mean Temperature (°F)
Mobile, Ala.	67.5
Boston, Mass.	51.3
Spokane, Wash.	47.3

Figure 1

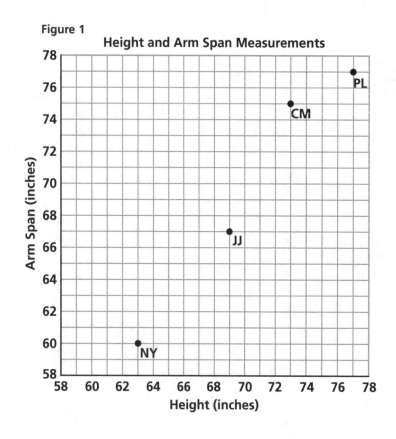

line plot A quick, simple way to organize data along a number line where the X's (or other symbols) above a number represent how often each value is mentioned.

Numbers of Siblings Students Have

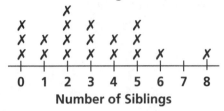

Number of Siblings

mean A value that represents the "evening out" of the values in a set of data. If all the data had the same value, the mean would be that value. For example, the total number of siblings for the above data is 56 siblings. If all 19 students had the same number of siblings, they would each have about 3 siblings. Differences from the mean "balance out" so that the sum of differences below and above the mean equal 0. The mean of a set of data is the sum of the values divided by the number of values in the set.

median The numerical value that marks the middle of an ordered set of data. Half the data occur above the median, and half the data occur below the median. The median of the distribution of siblings is 3 because the tenth (middle) value in the ordered set of 19 values (0, 0, 0, 1, 1, 2, 2, 2, 2, 3, 3, 3, 4, 4, 5, 5, 5, 6, 8) is 3 siblings.

mode The category or numerical value that occurs most often. The mode of the distribution of siblings is 2. It is possible for a set of data to have more than one mode.

numerical data Values that are numbers such as counts, measurements, and ratings. Here are some examples:

- Number of children in families
- Pulse rates (number of heart beats per minute)
- Height
- Amount of time people spend reading in one day
- Amount of value placed on something, such as: On a scale of 1 to 5 with 1 as "low interest," how would you rate your interest in participating in the school's field day?

outlier A value that lies far from the "center" of a distribution. Outlier is a relative term, but it indicates a data point that is much higher or much lower than the values that could be normally expected for the distribution.

R

range The difference between the least value and the greatest value in a distribution. For example, in the distribution below, the range of the number of siblings is 8 people.

Numbers of Siblings Students Have

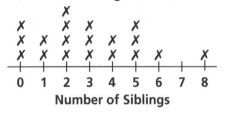

Number of Siblings

scale The size of the units on an axis of a graph or number line. For instance, each mark on the vertical axis might represent 10 units.

stem-and-leaf plot (stem plot) A quick way to picture the shape of a distribution while including the actual numerical values in the graph. For a number like 25, the stem 2 is written at the left of the vertical line, and the leaf 5 is at the right.

Travel Time

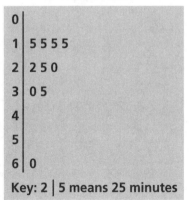

0	
1	5 5 5 5
2	2 5 0
3	0 5
4	
5	
6	0

Key: 2 | 5 means 25 minutes

survey A method for collecting data that uses interviews. Surveys ask questions to find out information such as facts, opinions, or beliefs.

table A tool for organizing information in rows and columns. Tables let you list categories or values and then tally the occurrences.

Favorite Colors

Color	Number of Students
Red	6
White	15
Blue	9

x-axis The horizontal number line used to make a graph.

y-axis The vertical number line used to make a graph.

Index

Answers to ACE Exercises
Investigation 1, 41–45
Investigation 2, 67–72
Investigation 3, 91–95

Answers to Investigation Problems
Investigation 1, 20, 26, 30, 36, 40
Investigation 2, 52, 56, 62, 66
Investigation 3, 80, 86, 90

At a Glance
Investigation 1, 19–20, 25–26, 29–30, 35–36, 39–40
Investigation 2, 51–52, 55–56, 61–62, 65–66
Investigation 3, 79–80, 85–86, 89–90

Assignment Guides
At a Glance, 20, 26, 30, 36, 40, 52, 56, 62, 66, 80, 86, 90
Investigation 1, 16, 41
Investigation 2, 46, 67
Investigation 3, 73, 91

Assessment Resources, 10, 12, 14

Blackline Masters
At a Glance Teacher Form, 106
Grid Paper, 105
Labsheets for Students, 103–104

Block Scheduling, 11

Connections to Other Units, 9

Correlations to Standardized Tests, 14

Glossary, 107–110

Launching the Unit, 15

Materials, 10
Investigation 1, 16
Investigation 2, 46
Investigation 3, 73

Mathematics Background, 3–8
Categorical Data, 4
Coordinate Graph, 7
Covariation, 8
Data Reduction, 6
Different Types of Data, 4
Distribution, 6
Frequency Bar Graph, 6
Line Plot, 6
Measures of Center, 7
Measures of Spread, 8
Numerical Data, 4
Standard Graphs, 6
Stem-and-Leaf Plot, 7

Mathematical Goals
Investigation 1, 16
Investigation 2, 46
Investigation 3, 73
Unit Goals, 2

Pacing Suggestions, 10–11
Investigation 1, 16
Investigation 2, 46
Investigation 3, 73

Planning for the Unit, 10
Investigation 1, 16
Investigation 2, 46
Investigation 3, 73

Program Resources, 12

Scoring Rubric, 97–101

Summary of Investigations, 3–4

Summary of Problems
Investigation 1, 16
Investigation 2, 46
Investigation 3, 73

Technology, 12

Unit Project, 15, 96

Vocabulary, 11

INDEX

Acknowledgments

Team Credits

The people who made up the **Connected Mathematics 2** team—representing editorial, editorial services, design services, and production services—are listed below. Bold type denotes core team members.

Leora Adler, Judith Buice, Kerry Cashman, Patrick Culleton, Sheila DeFazio, Richard Heater, **Barbara Hollingdale, Jayne Holman,** Karen Holtzman, **Etta Jacobs,** Christine Lee, Carolyn Lock, Catherine Maglio, **Dotti Marshall,** Rich McMahon, Eve Melnechuk, Kristin Mingrone, Terri Mitchell, **Marsha Novak,** Irene Rubin, Donna Russo, Robin Samper, Siri Schwartzman, **Nancy Smith,** Emily Soltanoff, **Mark Tricca,** Paula Vergith, Roberta Warshaw, Helen Young

Additional Credits

Diana Bonfilio, Mairead Reddin, Michael Torocsik, nSight, Inc.

Technical Illustration

Schawk, Inc.

Cover Design

tom white.images